UNIVERSITY MATHEMATICAL TEXTS

GENERAL EDITORS
ALEXANDER C. AITKEN, D.SC., F.R.S.
DANIEL E. RUTHERFORD, D.SC., DR. MATH.

ASSISTANT EDITOR
IAIN T. ADAMSON, PH.D.

29

NUMERICAL METHODS

I

ITERATION, PROGRAMMING AND ALGEBRAIC EQUATIONS

UNIVERSITY MATHEMATICAL TEXTS

NUMERICAL METHODS

I

ITERATION, PROGRAMMING
AND ALGEBRAIC EQUATIONS

BEN NOBLE
M.A., B.Sc., D.Sc., A.M.I.E.E.

THE MATHEMATICS RESEARCH CENTER, U.S. ARMY, THE UNIVERSITY OF
WISCONSIN, MADISON, WISCONSIN, U.S.A. (FORMERLY OF THE DEPARTMENT
OF MATHEMATICS, THE ROYAL COLLEGE OF SCIENCE AND TECHNOLOGY,
GLASGOW, SCOTLAND)

OLIVER AND BOYD
EDINBURGH AND LONDON
NEW YORK: INTERSCIENCE PUBLISHERS INC.

OLIVER AND BOYD LTD

Tweeddale Court
Edinburgh 1

39A Welbeck Street
London W.1

First published   1964
Reprinted   1966

PREFACE

It is desirable that all students of applied mathematics, the physical sciences, and engineering should be given an introduction to numerical analysis. The aim of this book is to provide, for this purpose, an elementary exposition of certain basic ideas. This has been done by considering a strictly limited selection of typical methods with particular emphasis on fundamentals, including error analysis, error estimation, pitfalls, and the detection of mistakes. An effort has been made to avoid the common practice of regarding numerical methods as a collection of algorithms or recipes. Rather than use a given amount of space to describe several different methods for solving the same type of problem, it has been thought preferable to illustrate general principles by discussing one single method in some detail. Numerical analysis should be a source of useful tools but it should also make the student think.

The advent of automatic computers has produced a revolution in computing. For this reason programming for computers has been made an integral part of the exposition. Although it is essential to teach the basic ideas of programming, the author believes that the time spent on the technical details in an elementary course should be cut to a minimum. There are advantages in teaching a simple general form of automatic programming or autocode of the type developed in Chapter III, which need occupy no more than one or two lectures. The system is not applicable to any particular machine but it contains many of the features common to autocodes. If it is preferred to teach a programming system used by an existing machine, the programs in

this book can easily be converted into the appropriate
autocode. (The word " program " is used in the technical
sense of a set of instructions specifying a procedure or
programme for solving a problem on a real or hypothetical
automatic computer.)

An automatic computer is indispensable for any institu-
tion concerned with the advanced teaching of scientists, but
the place which should be occupied by computers in teaching
elementary numerical analysis is likely to remain the subject
of debate for many years. One can visualise courses in
which all the practical work is done on automatic computers, and equally successful courses in which only hand
machines are used. It is instructive and stimulating for a
student to see a computer in operation but he need not
become a programmer to learn about numerical analysis.
Hand computing and automatic computing may require
different habits of thought, but the basic principles are
common and these can almost always be illustrated by
simple examples. Difficulties in large-scale calculations are
not usually due to the emergence of some radically new
kind of error. The main point is that all students should
have first-hand experience of numerical calculation, however this is obtained. There is usually a " correct " answer
to a problem in numerical mathematics in a precisely
defined sense. The onus is on the person specifying the
calculating procedure to ensure that the information
obtained during the computation will indicate in what sense,
if any, the calculation has resulted in an approximation to
the " correct " answer. It may help to impress this upon
the student if he sees an automatic computer produce,
without warning, numbers which are meaningless and
wrong, as the result of a program which he himself has
written.

When all computations have to be performed by hand,
the student tends to devote a major part of his effort to the
technical details of numerical procedures. When the

attitude is adopted that most calculations will be performed by computer, the emphasis in introductory courses can be shifted from the details of methods to the theory behind classes of methods. Though the student should have some acquaintance with the details of typical procedures, there is little point in teaching complicated algorithms to students who will normally meet such algorithms only in standard computer programs devised by experts. Thus the author would not normally teach Bairstow's method for finding the complex roots of polynomials (§ 2.7) in an elementary course.

Many examination questions on numerical methods are designed to test powers of regurgitation rather than understanding. The standard questions beginning " Describe a method for . . ." and " Find the solution of . . ." should not exclude other types of question, for example: " The calculations described below gave the following results. . . . Find out whether the required solution of the problem can be deduced from these results. In particular estimate the effect of truncation error (or round-off error, or instability of the method, or ill-conditioning of the original problem). Suggest methods for checking your conclusions."

It seems to be common practice to teach numerical analysis and basic mathematics in separate courses, and to postpone numerical analysis to a late stage—even a postgraduate stage—in a student's career. The author believes that this is wrong in principle and that much of the material in this book should ultimately be integrated into courses on basic mathematics for applied scientists. The material should be used to illustrate the mathematics, and to provide motivation and stimulation for more mathematics.

Operator methods for the derivation of finite-difference formulae have been omitted completely. Experience in teaching indicates that students quickly acquire facility in obtaining complicated formulae by operators without having much idea of the limitations or implications of their results. It seems preferable in an introductory course to concentrate attention on the basic underlying principle, namely that functions are being represented by polynomials through equally spaced points. Other types of functional representation can be introduced as natural alternatives.

Most error estimates have been obtained in the form of a dominant term followed by a series of dots. Little attempt has been made to obtain closed error estimates by using a Taylor series with a remainder term, or mean-value theorems, since at an elementary level this complicates the analysis without contributing materially to the understanding of either the method or the results. Questions of elegance and rigour enter into the discussion of a numerical method but this book is not aimed at the pure mathematician. In some ways numerical analysis should be approached as if it were an experimental science. An exact answer exists for any given problem, and the numerical analyst attempts to determine this exact answer, to a specified degree of accuracy, by means of suitably designed experiments. Mathematics is the tool, but not the aim or object, of the science.

Short chapters are included on eigenvalues and partial differential equations. These are topics which are normally regarded as " advanced ", but from a numerical point of view they can be treated in almost as elementary a fashion as the solution of algebraic equations, or ordinary differential equations.

For further reading it is recommended that the student start with *Modern Computing Methods*, H.M. Stationery Office, 2nd. Edn. (1961), which both supplements and complements the present text, and includes a list of papers and books. In view of the comprehensive bibliography in *Modern Computing Methods* it has seemed unnecessary to include more than a few (non-systematic) references in the present text.

Unless otherwise indicated the numerical examples have

been worked on a hand-machine, and as a general rule one extra decimal place has been carried in the intermediate working. When the student checks numerical examples his results may of course differ slightly from those in the text in the last significant digit. Many of the examples at the ends of chapters are intended to supplement the text, not to provide additional exercises.

The origins of this book can be traced back to the lectures of the late D. R. Hartree, and a year spent in the Mathematical Laboratory, Cambridge, under M. V. Wilkes in 1947-48 during the exciting early days of EDSAC. Even though this experience failed to convert me into a professional computer, it taught me that numerical analysis is much more than an exercise in pure mathematics or a collection of recipes.

The preparation of the manuscript of this book was a time-consuming occupation. I feel indebted to the mathematics department of the future second university in Glasgow, to my wife, and to all correspondents who have had to wait for answers to letters. They had much to endure while the second draft of this book was being typed with one finger.

It is a pleasure to acknowledge help from many friends. The ideas in Chapter III on programming for automatic computers originated from using the system known as FORTRAN (FORmula TRANslation) on the IBM 704 at the New York University AEC Computing Facility. I am grateful to E. Isaacson for encouragement to use this machine and to Max Goldstein for indispensable advice. The work was made possible by contract AF 19(604)5238 of the Electronics Directorate of the U.S. Air Force Cambridge Research Centre, which financed a visit to the Division of Electromagnetic Research, the Institute of Mathematical Sciences, New York University. A first draft of Chapter III was considerably altered after correspondence with T. Brooker and S. Gill, and a subsequent meeting with members of the committee on automatic programming of the British Computer Society, chairman C. Strachey.

A remark of T. Brooker changed the emphasis of Chapter II from " solution of equations " to " iterative procedures ". D. J. Wheeler introduced me to the idea of the " noise-level " of an iterative calculation. Various comments in the text on the representation of functions by polynomials have been modified as a result of criticisms by G. F. Miller. Several points have been clarified by discussions with A. J. Howie, G. N. Lance, A. van Wijngaarden and J. H. Wilkinson.

Many of the numerical examples have been checked by A. Paton and M. V. Sweet. Numerical results have been contributed by: J. G. Fraser and M. V. Sweet (Ex. 10.23), A. Paton (Table 4.1), M. Walker (Ex. 11.8), F. J. Warner (Ex. 10.17), S. B. L. Wilson (the table (11.26)), C. S. Wu (Ex. 10.22).

A. C. Aitken, J. G. Fraser and M. V. Sweet have spent much time in reading the manuscript in painstaking detail. Their valuable criticisms have increased the accuracy and readability of the text and the examples. G. Fairweather, R. C. Peebles and B. Shaw have assisted in proof-reading and contributed helpful comments. D. Greenspan has suggested improvements and detected inaccuracies in both manuscript and proofs. I am indebted to the editors, A. C. Aitken and D. E. Rutherford, for advice and recommendations.

Above all I am grateful to Miss A. Paton. In a period of numerous distractions her assistance ensured a regular weekly production of manuscript. It is certain that without her help this book would never have been written.

B. NOBLE

MILL COTTAGE,
BROUGHTON MILLS, LANCS.
July, 1962.

CONTENTS

VOLUME II.—DIFFERENCES INTEGRATION AND DIFFERENTIAL EQUATIONS

VII. FINITE DIFFERENCES AND THE APPROXIMATE REPRE-
SENTATION OF FUNCTIONS

VIII. POLYNOMIAL INTERPOLATION

IX. NUMERICAL INTEGRATION AND DIFFERENTIATION

X. ORDINARY DIFFERENTIAL EQUATIONS

XI. PARTIAL DIFFERENTIAL EQUATIONS

CHAPTER I

ACCURACY AND ERROR

§ 1.1. Introduction. The solution of a problem in applied mathematics usually consists of numbers which satisfy some kind of equation. In theory these numbers may be specified exactly by the equation but even in the simplest cases (of which $x = \sqrt{2}$ can be taken as a trivial example) it is normally impossible to write down an exact decimal representation of the solution. *The aim of numerical methods is to provide practical procedures for calculating the solutions of problems in applied mathematics to a specified degree of accuracy.*

We shall be constantly preoccupied with the estimation and prevention of errors. This is merely recognition of the fact that to produce a number which is the answer to a problem is only half the aim of numerical methods. The other half, and often the more difficult half, is to ensure that the answer is correct within stated limits. Any numerical answer should be accompanied by a statement of its maximum error or its probable error.

Errors occur in computation in four ways:

(a) Round-off errors due to the need to represent numbers in decimal notation, using a finite number of decimal places.

(b) Mistakes.

(c) Errors due to the nature of the formulae used, e.g. the need to represent a continuous function by a table of numbers.

(d) Some of the numbers which must be used in the
    computation may have inherent error, or may be
    known only approximately, e.g. physical data.

It is a most important principle in numerical work that
all sources of error must be borne constantly in mind.

§ **1.2.   Rounding off.**   The numbers 0·745 25 and
0·007 452 5 are given to five and seven decimal places
respectively.   The number of **significant figures** is defined
as the number of digits that are assumed to be correct,
starting at the left with the first non-zero digit, and proceed-
ing to the right.   Thus if all the non-zero digits in the above
numbers are correct, they both possess five significant
figures.   Zeros to the left of the first non-zero digit are not
significant and serve merely to mark the decimal point.
Zeros to the right of the last non-zero digit are regarded as
significant.   Thus 0·4300 possesses four significant figures.
Ambiguity occurs with a number like 4300.   This can be
written $4·300 \times 10^3$ if it is desired to indicate that it is
correct to four significant figures. $4·30 \times 10^3$ is correct to
three significant figures.

If only certain digits in a number are correct the
superfluous digits can be discarded by **rounding off.**   The
rule for doing this is as follows.   To round off a number to
n significant figures retain n significant digits and discard
the remainder.   If the discarded number is less than half a
unit in the nth place leave the nth digit unchanged: if it
is greater than half a unit in the nth place add unity to the
nth digit: if it is exactly half a unit round off to the nearest
even digit.   The object of the last part of the rule is to
ensure that when exactly half a digit is discarded, numbers
will be rounded up and rounded down in equal proportions,
on the average.   The only reason for rounding to even
rather than to odd digits is that the resulting number is
divisible by two without ambiguity.   If 7·4525 is rounded

off to 4, 3, 2 figures we obtain 7·452, 7·45, 7·5. But note that if 7·45 is rounded off to two significant figures, without further information, we obtain 7·4.

§ **1.3. Absolute and relative errors.** If n is an approximation to a number N which is defined exactly, the **error** ε of n is defined by $N = n + \varepsilon$. (Some writers use the definition $n = N + \varepsilon$ but the distinction is not important though it is better to be consistent.) The **absolute error** is $|\varepsilon|$ and the (absolute) **relative error** is $|\varepsilon|/|N|$. We shall be interested in comparatively rough estimates of the error and we assume that the relative error is small. In this case the relative error can be taken equal to $|\varepsilon|/|n|$ which has the advantage that the denominator is known.

It is often possible to establish an upper limit for the magnitude of the error. For example if a number is given to exactly m decimal places then $|\varepsilon| \leqq 0 \cdot 5 \times 10^{-m}$. We call this upper limit for the magnitude of the error the **maximum error** and denote it by e. Thus $|\varepsilon| \leqq e$. The relative error is less than $e/|N| \approx e/|n|$ (assuming that e is much less than $|n|$).

Let n_1, n_2 be approximations to N_1, N_2 with errors ε_1, ε_2, so that

$$N_1 = n_1 + \varepsilon_1, \qquad N_2 = n_2 + \varepsilon_2.$$

Consider first addition and subtraction:

$$N_1 + N_2 = (n_1 + n_2) + (\varepsilon_1 + \varepsilon_2),$$
$$N_1 - N_2 = (n_1 - n_2) + (\varepsilon_1 - \varepsilon_2).$$

If $|\varepsilon_1| < e_1$, $|\varepsilon_2| < e_2$, then $|\varepsilon_1 + \varepsilon_2| < e_1 + e_2$, $|\varepsilon_1 - \varepsilon_2| < e_1 + e_2$. Hence *if two numbers are added or subtracted, the maximum error in the sum or difference is the sum of the maximum errors in the two numbers.* For multiplication we have

$$N_1 N_2 = n_1 n_2 + n_2 \varepsilon_1 + n_1 \varepsilon_2 + \varepsilon_1 \varepsilon_2.$$

accurate to 1 in 600. Although the less accurate number in each of these examples is given to three significant figures it would be misleading and inaccurate to round-off the answers to three significant figures.

§ **1.4. Error analysis and control.** When using a desk calculating machine, round-off errors are under the direct control of the person doing the computation. It would be tiresome to have to round off every single number in a calculation to the appropriate number of significant figures. On the other hand it is essential to employ round-off to save unnecessary labour and keep the lengths of numbers within reasonable limits. One difficulty is illustrated by the calculation $0 \cdot 014\ 63 \div 79 \cdot 3 = 0 \cdot 000\ 184\ 5$. To obtain an answer correct to 1 in 1000 it is necessary to carry seven decimal places in the answer. On the other hand if we can scale our variables so that the calculation reads $1 \cdot 463 \div 0 \cdot 793 = 1 \cdot 845$ we need carry only three decimals. It is desirable to arrange, by scaling or otherwise, that in the body of the calculation all numbers are rounded to $n+1$ or $n+2$ decimal places and that this then gives an answer correct to n decimals. A more elaborate example of scaling is given in § 4.1, Ex. 4.1.

A similar situation can arise in connection with automatic digital computers. These machines perform essentially the same arithmetic operations as a desk calculator—they add, subtract, multiply and divide numbers stored inside the machine (see § 3.1). Analysis of round-off errors will depend on the way in which numbers are stored. If a **fixed-point** system is used this means that numbers are represented with a fixed number of decimal places e.g. $0 \cdot 0015$, $793 \cdot 1482$. If a **floating-point** system is used numbers are represented with a fixed number of significant figures e.g. $1 \cdot 463 \times 10^{-3}$, $7 \cdot 931 \times 10^{2}$, where we have placed the decimal point immediately after the first significant digit. The scaling difficulty mentioned in the last paragraph may be particularly important if calculations have to be performed in a fixed-point system.

In hand computing it is possible to vary the number of decimal places being carried in the light of the results obtained as the calculation proceeds in order to obtain an answer of the required accuracy with the minimum of labour. In automatic computing the number of decimals depends on the design of the machine and it may be difficult to predict beforehand the course of a calculation. It is often easier to make the machine compute as accurate an answer as possible, subject to round-off and other errors, and then determine the accuracy that has been achieved, rather than try to produce an answer of specified accuracy.

It is important to realise that calculations can often be arranged so that the effect of round-off errors is minimised. This is illustrated in the following two examples.

Ex. 1.1. *Find the roots of* $x^2 - 26x + 1 = 0$.

We have $x = 13 \pm \sqrt{168} = 13 \pm 12 \cdot 961$. Hence the roots are $x_1 = 25 \cdot 961$, $x_2 = 0 \cdot 039$. The second root has been obtained to only two significant figures even though the square root was calculated to five figures. However, instead of calculating the second root in this way we can use the relation $x_1 x_2 = 1$, so that $x_2 = 1/25 \cdot 961 = 0 \cdot 038\ 519$, in error by at most one unit in the last digit.

Ex. 1.2. *Evaluate* $\qquad c = \dfrac{bA - aB}{b - a},$ \hfill (1.1)

with $b = 0 \cdot 485$, $a = 0 \cdot 231$, $B = 6 \cdot 327\ 19$, $A = 6 \cdot 322\ 81$, *where the data are accurate only to the number of figures stated.*

If we use the formula for c as it stands, it might seem that the result will be accurate to only three significant figures since the denominator is accurate to only 1 in 250.

However, if we rearrange the formula in the form

$$c = A - \frac{a(B-A)}{b-a} \qquad (1.2)$$

we find, on substituting numbers and carrying out a rough error analysis, that $c = 6 \cdot 318\ 83$, correct to within two units in the last digit quoted. If we substitute directly in the original formula (1.1) and carry sufficient places in the intermediate working we find

$$c = 1 \cdot 604\ 982 / 0 \cdot 254 = 6 \cdot 318\ 83.$$

This is the same answer as before, accurate to two units in the last digit quoted, even though we know that the denominator is accurate to only 1 in 250. The reason is clear on performing an error analysis algebraically. Suppose that the exact value of a is given by $a + \delta a$, and similarly for b, A, B, c. Then on neglecting second order quantities it is found that

$$\delta c = \frac{(b+\delta b)(A+\delta A)-(a+\delta a)(B+\delta B)}{(b-a)+(\delta b-\delta a)} - \frac{bA-aB}{b-a}$$

$$\approx \{(B-A)(a\delta b - b\delta a) + (b-a)(b\delta A - a\delta B)\}(b-a)^{-2}.$$

Terms involving A and B have cancelled to give a final error which depends only on $(B-A)$, δA, and δB, all of which are small. Substitution in this formula again gives the maximum possible error as two units in the fifth decimal place.

Formula (1.2) is more convenient than (1.1) since the error can be estimated more directly from it, and since fewer decimal places need be carried in the computation to obtain a given accuracy in the final answer. This is an important example of the way in which a formula can be rearranged to give a more suitable formula for computation.

Error analysis in terms of maximum error, as discussed in the last section, is useful in avoiding particular sources of error, but in a long calculation an error analysis worked out on the basis of the maximum possible error will over-estimate the errors which are likely to occur in practice by a very large factor. For instance if the maximum absolute error of a single result is e then the maximum possible error that can be obtained when adding n numbers is ne, though this is very unlikely to occur in practice. In fact if errors are randomly distributed between $\pm e$, there is only one chance in 20 that the error in the sum of n numbers will exceed $2(n/3)^{\frac{1}{2}}e$, assuming that the errors in the n numbers are independent. There is only one chance in 370 that the error will exceed $3(n/3)^{\frac{1}{2}}e$, and this number is much less than ne if n is large. More precisely, the following results are given by statistical theory.† The details lie outside the scope of this book. If errors are distributed around zero according to a frequency distribution $y = f(x)$, the variance of the error in a single number is defined to be

$$\sigma^2 = \int_{-\infty}^{\infty} x^2 f(x)dx, \quad \left(\int_{-\infty}^{\infty} f(x)dx = 1 \right).$$

The variance of the error in the sum of n numbers is $n\sigma^2$ and the standard deviation of the error of the sum is the square root of the variance, or $n^{\frac{1}{2}}\sigma$. The distribution of the sum tends to the normal or Gaussian form as n increases. Thus there is only one chance in 20 of obtaining an error of more than twice the standard deviation. As an application of these results suppose that errors are uniformly distributed between ± 0.5, so that $f(x) = 1$, $-0.5 < x < 0.5$, and $f(x) = 0$ for $|x| > 0.5$. Then

$$\sigma^2 = \int_{-0.5}^{0.5} x^2 dx = \tfrac{1}{12}.$$

The standard deviation of the error of the sum of n numbers is therefore $(n/12)^{\frac{1}{2}}$. On adding 100 numbers the standard

† A. C. Aitken, *Statistical Mathematics*, Oliver and Boyd (1942), pp. 35, 62.

deviation is approximately 3 and if the errors are randomly distributed it is unlikely that the total error will be more than ± 6. It is very unlikely that the error will be more than ± 10. In contrast, the maximum possible error is ± 50. Statistical considerations are particularly important in connection with automatic computers, where calculations may involve an extremely large number of operations.

From an analogy with noise in an electrical circuit, round-off errors which occur at random can be regarded as " noise " superimposed on an exact calculation. Some interesting comments on round-off noise are given in R. W. Hamming, *Numerical Methods for Scientists and Engineers*, McGraw-Hill (1962), Chapter II. It is also pointed out in this chapter that in many circumstances the size of the leading (i.e. most significant) digit in the numbers of a calculation may tend to be small. Thus if two numbers are multiplied together, each being chosen at random from 1, 2, ... 9, then by examining the leading digits in the 81 possible products it is easily seen that it is probable that the leading digit will be a number with a small leading digit.

A theoretical analysis of error, statistical or otherwise, is invaluable when comparing the relative efficiencies of various methods for solving a given type of problem. Even when it is possible to estimate errors within useful limits, however, we are usually interested in the actual error in the answer to a specific concrete example rather than the average or maximum error when the method is applied to a class of examples. For this reason we shall not devote much space in this book to the determination of maximum or average errors in computing procedures. Instead the following approach is adopted. After a general analysis of the sources of error in a given method, the numerical procedure is arranged so that an estimate of the accuracy of the answer can be obtained empirically from the results obtained during the course of the calculation. Some of the ways in which this can be done will be explained later in connection with particular examples, but the general principle is stated here to emphasise that from the point of view adopted in this book the object of theoretical error analysis is practical error control.

§ **1.5. The evaluation of formulae on desk machines.** It will be assumed in this section that the reader is familiar with the operation of an ordinary desk calculator possessing a setting register, a multiplier register, and an accumulator. For example, in forming the product ab the number a is inserted in the setting register. When this number is multiplied by b the number b appears in the multiplier register and the product ab in the accumulator.

Without going into detail we emphasise briefly several aspects of the use of such machines, with particular reference to the way in which good machine technique can prevent the occurrence of mistakes. An elementary example occurs in connection with reading negative numbers off the machine. Negative numbers appear in the accumulator as complements, for example 99 . . . 994 732 represents the number -5268. In reading such a number off the machine, the safe procedure is to set the complement, calculated mentally, (namely 5268), in the setting register; add into the accumulator; check that the accumulator then reads zero, and record the number in the setting register. Another example occurs in connection with transferring numbers from the accumulator to the setting register. The number which is entered in the setting register should be checked in an obvious way by subtracting it from the contents of the accumulator.

On the whole it is a good idea to do as much work as possible on the machine. For instance unnecessary recording of numbers should be avoided. Thus $a \times b \times c$ and $a \times b \div c$ can be calculated without recording inter-mediate numbers. Similarly expressions like

$$a_1 b_1 + a_2 b_2 + a_3 b_3 + \ldots$$

can be calculated without intermediate recording. In this type of calculation (as in any calculation involving a repetitive procedure) it is essential to fix the positions of the decimal points in the setting register, the multiplier register, and the accumulator, subject of course to the condition that $1 \cdot 0 \times 1 \cdot 0 = 1 \cdot 0$.

Care has to be exercised when transferring numbers from the work sheet to a calculating machine or vice-versa, or from one part of the sheet to another. Common errors occur from transposing digits (e.g. 8452 may be transferred as 8542), or from repeated digits (e.g. 8455 may be transferred as 8445).

Wherever possible the work should be reduced to a routine. Tabulation is a great help in this respect. It is usually best to arrange a tabulation so as to do only one thing at a time. Differencing procedures are often useful in checking (§ 7.3).

Ex. 1.3. *Find $f(1 \cdot 518)$ by linear interpolation, given that*

$$f(1 \cdot 300) = 0 \cdot 752\ 15, \qquad f(1 \cdot 600) = 0 \cdot 746\ 39.$$

Also find the value of x for which $f(x) = 0 \cdot 750\ 61$.

If we wish to evaluate $y = f(x)$ by **linear interpolation** given $y_1 = f(x_1)$ and $y_2 = f(x_2)$, we mean that we wish to evaluate y assuming that the point (x, y) lies on the straight line joining (x_1, y_1) and (x_2, y_2). It is easily verified that the required formula is

$$y = \{(x_1 - x)y_0 + (x - x_0)y_1\}/(x_1 - x_0). \qquad (1.3)$$

For computational purposes it is desirable to rearrange this formula as

$$y = y_0 + p(y_1 - y_0), \qquad p = (x - x_0)/(x_1 - x_0). \quad (1.4)$$

(This has been explained in Ex. 1.2. Compare (1.1), (1.3) and (1.2), (1.4) with $b = (x_1 - x)$, $a = (x_0 - x)$, $B = y_1$, $A = y_0$).

In this example $h = 0.218/0.300 = 0.727$, to three figures. A safe procedure on a calculating machine is as follows. Set $0.752\,15$. Multiply by 1.000, where we use three decimal places since h is specified to three places. Clear the multiplier register. Calculate $y_1 - y_0$ mentally ($-0.005\,76$). Set $0.005\,76$ and turn the handle once backward (since $y_1 - y_0$ is negative). Check that the accumulator now reads $f(1.6) = 0.746\,39$. This checks the setting of $f(1.3)$ and the mental calculation of $y_1 - y_0$, including its sign. The multiplier register now reads 1.000. Turn the handle until it shows 0.727. The number in the accumulator is $f(1.518) = 0.747\,96$, rounded to five decimals.

To answer the last part of the question, which involves " inverse linear interpolation ", turn the handle till the accumulator shows the number nearest to $0.750\,61$. The number in the multiplier register is then 0.267. The required value of x is therefore $1.300 + 0.3 \times 0.267 = 1.380$, to three decimal places.

Ex. 1.4. *Evaluate the following polynomials to four decimal places for $x = 0(0.2)1.0$:*

$$f_1(x) = x - \tfrac{1}{3}x^3 + \tfrac{1}{5}x^5,$$

$$f_2(x) = 0.995\,36x - 0.288\,69x^3 + 0.079\,34x^5,$$

$$f_3(x) = 0.994\,95x - 0.287\,06x^3 + 0.078\,04x^5.$$

Compare the results with the corresponding values of $f(x) = \text{arc tan } x$.

The notation $x = a(p)b$ means " from the value $x = a$ to the value $x = b$, inclusive, at intervals of p in x ". Since four decimal places are required in the answer, five decimals should be carried in the working. We write

$$f_1(x) = \tfrac{1}{3}x(3 - x^2 + 0.6x^4).$$

The values of $f_1(x)$ can be found systematically by means

of a tabulation with the following headings:

$$x \qquad \tfrac{1}{3}x \qquad x^2 \qquad x^4 \qquad f_1(x)$$

The value of $\tfrac{1}{3}x$ is calculated mentally. The values of x^2 and x^4 can be obtained from *Barlow's Tables*.† The value of $f_1(x)$ is obtained in one desk machine operation involving two additions and two multiplications. Three numbers are recorded in addition to x and $f_1(x)$. It is convenient to set x^2, x^4 on the machine and to use $0\cdot6$ and $\tfrac{1}{3}x$ as multipliers.

For $f_2(x)$ we can proceed similarly except that it is slightly more convenient to write

$$f_2(x) = x(0\cdot995\,36 - 0\cdot288\,69x^2 + 0\cdot079\,34x^4)$$

and the table heading $\tfrac{1}{3}x$ is now omitted. The evaluation of $f_2(x)$ is carried out in one machine operation involving three multiplications and one addition. Two recordings are required besides x and $f_2(x)$. It is convenient in this case to set the five decimal place coefficients in the setting register, and multiply by x^2, x^4.

If we had to evaluate $f_2(x)$ for $x = 0(0\cdot1\pi)0\cdot5\pi$, say, then x^2, x^4 would have to be computed on the desk machine so that the procedure in the last paragraph would require five multiplications and one addition. In this case we should probably prefer to use nested multiplication:

$$a_1x + a_3x^3 + a_5x^5 = x\{a_1 + u(a_3 + a_5u)\},$$

where $u = x^2$. This requires four multiplications and two additions. Only one recording is required besides x and $f_2(x)$. In hand computing, the number of decimal places and significant figures needed at various stages of the calculation have a decisive effect on the organisation of the calculation. In an automatic computer all numbers are treated alike irrespective of the number of significant figures

† Edited by L. J. Comrie, E. & F. Spon (London) (1952).

they contain, and the method used for evaluating a polynomial will not depend on whether the coefficients or the values of x are simple.

The polynomial $f_1(x)$ consists of the first three terms of the Taylor series expansion of arc tan x. The accuracy of a truncated Taylor series decreases with increase in the distance from the point about which the function is expanded. This is illustrated by the numerical results in Table 1.1. The polynomial $f_2(x)$ gives a much better approximation over the whole range of x although it is not so accurate as $f_1(x)$

TABLE 1.1

Results for Exercise 1.4

x	0·2	0·4	0·6	0·8	1·0
$f(x)$	0·1974	0·3805	0·5404	0·6747	0·7854
$f(x)-f_1(x)$	0	−2	−32	−201	−813
$f(x)-f_2(x)$	+6	0	−6	+2	−6
$f(x)-f_3(x)$	+7	+1	−6	+1	−5

near $x = 0$. The polynomial $f_3(x)$ is derived in Ex. 7.5 by truncating a Chebyshev series. It is almost as good a representation of arc tan x over the whole range as the polynomial $f_2(x)$ which is the optimum polynomial in the minimax sense explained in § 7.5. (See also Ex. 3.6 and the reference given there.) Polynomial representations like $f_2(x), f_3(x)$ are particularly useful in automatic computing.

§ **1.6. Mistakes.** The main part of this section is concerned with mistakes due to faulty computing technique when using a desk calculating machine. No matter how carefully a computation is performed there is always some risk that mistakes will occur and it is essential to include checks throughout a calculation to ensure that mistakes will be detected as quickly as possible.

Experience is the best teacher in showing the beginner where mistakes are likely to occur and how mistakes can be avoided. It is sufficient to mention some of the more obvious sources of error—illegible figures, untidy arrangement (particularly when figures are arranged in columns), unsystematic work, trying to do too many steps at once.

To some extent computing technique will depend on the individual and the following notes represent personal preferences. It is convenient to work in ink on paper ruled in rectangular boxes, or on squared paper with numbers inserted in suitable boxes formed from the squares. A mistake is corrected by drawing a line through a wrong number and inserting the corrected value above the wrong one. This is to be preferred to the use of pencil and rubber for various reasons. Use of ink encourages accuracy. It is useful to know when mistakes have been corrected, and exactly what corrections have been made, partly because it is easy to make further errors when correcting mistakes. Apart from anything else the work-sheet will soon look unsightly if too many mistakes are made and this is a sign that the computer should take more care—or even start again from the beginning.

A point that is often neglected is to include sufficient explanation on the sheets—a calculation should be intelligible a year later. It is advisable to include details of all the steps in the calculation in sequence—scribbling in odd corners of the sheet to obtain intermediate results is to be discouraged. It is precisely in these intermediate results that mistakes are likely to occur.

When an answer has been obtained it may be easy to check whether it is correct, for example by substitution. On the other hand the only method of checking may be to repeat the calculation. (Straightforward repetition by the same person is *not* satisfactory since there may be a tendency to repeat certain kinds of mistake if a calculation is repeated in the same form by the same person.) Between these two extremes it is not unreasonable to ask that ten or twenty per cent of the time spent on a calculation should be devoted to checks. It is often convenient to arrange a calculation so that a difference check can be employed (§ 7.3). One has to be doubly careful when considering the correctness of results obtained by means of automatic computers since usually an automatic machine produces answers without any detailed information about intermediate steps. It is therefore very easy to be unaware of loss of accuracy due to the particular way in which the calculations have been performed inside the machine.

It is important to try to develop a kind of " numerical common-sense " to detect obvious blunders and to keep a mental check whether the results of a calculation are turning out as one would expect.

The length of time taken over a computation is of little importance compared with the necessity for obtaining a correct answer.

Examples I

Ex. 1.5. Perform each of the following calculations on a desk machine without recording intermediate results. State the accuracy of each answer and round off to the appropriate number of significant digits:

$$4 \cdot 0963 - 53 \cdot 41 - 492 \cdot 0 + 63 \cdot 415,$$

$$(93 \cdot 05 \times 4 \cdot 0732) - (62 \cdot 14 \times 0 \cdot 2154) - (676 \times 0 \cdot 0873),$$

$$2 \cdot 4076 \times 0 \cdot 049\ 18 \times 0 \cdot 000\ 963,$$

$$(0 \cdot 4362 \times 0 \cdot 029\ 432) \div 0 \cdot 007\ 44.$$

Ex. 1.6. Find $\sqrt{39} - \sqrt{38}$ to five significant figures, given $\sqrt{39} = 6 \cdot 2450$, $\sqrt{38} = 6 \cdot 1644$.

Ex. 1.7. A change of δx in x produces a change of approximately $(df/dx)\delta x$ in $f(x)$. Hence show that if in the determination of cot 0·128 the argument is correct to the number of figures stated, the cotangent is indeterminate to within 0·03. Check this result by finding from tables the values of cot 0·128 and cot 0·1285. Similarly find the degree of determinacy in the following quantities:

$$\sin 1{\cdot}560, \; \cos 1{\cdot}560, \; \tan^{-1} 15{\cdot}0, \; \log 1{\cdot}083, \; \exp(-2{\cdot}031).$$

Find also the number of significant figures in each quantity and check your results from tables. (The point of this example is to remind the reader that when $y = f(x)$ is read from a table the number of significant figures in y is not necessarily the same as the number of significant figures in x.)

Ex. 1.8. Evaluate $\theta (\cosh \theta - \cos \theta)/(\sinh \theta - \sin \theta)$ to five significant figures for $\theta = 0.3741$ by expanding appropriate terms as power series in θ.

Ex. 1.9. Distinguish between fixed- and floating-point calculations and compare the maximum errors involved in the two systems when computing (i) the sum of n numbers (ii) the product of n numbers (iii) the sum of n products of the form $a_i b_i$.

CHAPTER II

ITERATIVE METHODS, WITH APPLICATIONS TO THE SOLUTION OF EQUATIONS

§ **2.1.** **Introduction.** In this chapter we introduce an important class of numerical procedures, namely iterative methods. These are illustrated by describing typical iterative procedures for solving transcendental and algebraic equations. (Equations like $\cot x = 2x$, $x \ln x = 4$, containing transcendental functions, are called transcendental equations. A simple algebraic equation is $x^3 = 3x + 2$. All of these equations can be written in the form $f(x) = 0$.)

The first step in an iterative solution of an equation $f(x) = 0$ is to locate the roots approximately. An easy method for locating any real roots is to draw a graph of the function $y = f(x)$ and find the points where the curve cuts the x-axis. Sometimes it is convenient to write $f(x) = 0$ in the form $f_1(x) = f_2(x)$ and to plot two functions $y = f_1(x)$ and $y = f_2(x)$. The real roots of $f(x) = 0$ are given by the abscissae of the points of intersection of the two graphs.

Various methods are available for the numerical solution of equations and it lies outside the scope of this short book to describe and compare even the more important of these. It is not implied in this chapter that the iterative methods which we discuss are to be preferred to any other methods for solving equations numerically. If an equation is complicated and results are required to only a few decimal places there may be little point in using, for instance, a rapidly convergent iterative method like the Newton-Raphson process of § 2.3. It may be much more convenient and satisfactory to use repeated plotting on successively enlarged scales (compare the last paragraph) or the method of false position (Ex. 2.12). On the other hand, when finding the complex roots of high-order polynomials it may be desirable to use sophisticated methods such as those of Graeffe or Bernoulli.

§ 2.2. A simple iterative method. Consider the equation

$$x^2 - 5x + 2 = 0 \qquad (2.1)$$

which has the roots α, β, say, where

$$\alpha = 2\cdot5 - \sqrt{4\cdot25} = 0\cdot438\,447,$$
$$\beta = 2\cdot5 + \sqrt{4\cdot25} = 4\cdot561\,553.$$

In order to illustrate a simple iterative procedure we shall solve (2.1) in the following way. The first step is to localise the roots approximately. By evaluating $y = x^2 - 5x + 2$ for $x = 0, 1, 2, \ldots$ we find that (2.1) has one root between 0 and 1, and one root between 4 and 5. We then rearrange (2.1) in the form

$$x = 0\cdot2x^2 + 0\cdot4.$$

This equation can be solved iteratively by writing

$$x_{r+1} = 0\cdot2x_r^2 + 0\cdot4, \quad r = 0, 1, 2, \ldots \qquad (2.2)$$

where x_r denotes the rth approximation to a root. We start by choosing, say, $x_0 = 0$ as an approximation to one of the roots of the quadratic. If this is substituted on the right of (2.2) we obtain $x_1 = 0\cdot4$. This value is then substituted on the right of (2.2) to give x_2, and so on. In this way we find

$$x_2 = 0\cdot432, \quad x_3 = 0\cdot437\,32, \quad x_4 = 0\cdot438\,25, \quad (2.3)$$

where in the last two calculations we have worked to five decimal places. It is clear that, as r increases, x_r is approaching the smaller root α of the quadratic. If on the other hand we start with $x_0 = 10$ we find

$$x_1 = 20 \cdot 4, \quad x_2 = 83 \cdot 6, \quad x_3 = 1398 \cdot 2,$$

and as r increases x_r increases without limit. Before considering the reasons for these results we give some definitions.

A calculation of the form

$$x_{r+1} = F(x_r), \qquad r = 0, 1, 2, ..., \qquad (2.4)$$

where we start from an assumed value for x_0, and then calculate x_1, x_2, ... in succession, as indicated in the example above, is called an **iterative procedure.** If as r tends to infinity x_r tends to a definite value then the procedure is said to **converge.** If as r tends to infinity x_r does not converge (for example if x_r tends to infinity) then the procedure is said to **diverge.**

We examine theoretically the convergence of the iterative procedure (2.4) by a method which will be useful in later sections. On setting $x = x_r + \delta x_r$, where x is an exact root, equation (2.4) becomes

$$x - \delta x_{r+1} = F(x - \delta x_r). \qquad (2.5a)$$

From (2.4), if the procedure converges,

$$x = F(x), \qquad (2.5b)$$

On expanding the right-hand side of (2.5a) in a Taylor series and using (2.5b) we find

$$\delta x_{r+1} = \delta x_r F'(x) - \tfrac{1}{2} \delta x_r^2 F''(x) + ... \qquad (2.6a)$$

In this section we assume that $F'(x)$ is non-zero. When the difference between x and x_r is small we can ignore the higher-order terms on the right of (2.6a) which then gives

$$\delta x_{r+1} \approx \delta x_r F'(x). \qquad (2.6b)$$

c

Repeated application of this formula gives

$$\delta x_{r+1} \approx [F'(x)]^{r+1}\delta x_0.$$

Hence if $|F'(x)| < 1$ we obtain the result that δx_r tends to zero as r tends to infinity i.e. the iterative procedure converges.

A more rigorous derivation is the following. Instead of the infinite Taylor series which led to (2.6a) we use the Taylor series with remainder (or equally the mean value theorem for derivatives)†:

$$F(x-\delta x_r) = F(x)-\delta x_r F'(\xi),$$

where ξ lies in the range x to $x_r = x-\delta x_r$. It is assumed that $F'(\xi)$ exists in this range and that $F(\xi)$ is continuous in the range including the end-points. Then (2.5a, b) give, instead of (2.6),

$$\delta x_{r+1} = \delta x_r F'(\xi)$$

where ξ lies between x and x_r. Suppose that

$$|F'(\xi)| < M \tag{2.7}$$

for the range of ξ in which we are interested, where M is a constant independent of r. Then

$$|\delta x_{r+1}| < M|\delta x_r| < M^{r+1}|\delta x_0|. \tag{2.8}$$

If $M < 1$ then δx_r tends to zero as r tends to infinity. A sufficient condition for convergence of the iterative procedure (2.4) is therefore that $|F'(\xi)| < 1$ for ξ near the required root.

It is instructive to illustrate this result graphically as in Fig. 2.1(a-d) where we have drawn $y = x$ and $y = F(x)$ for several different functions $F(x)$. Starting from an arbitrary value x_0 of x on the line $y = x$ we move vertically to the curve $y = F(x)$ and then horizontally back to the line $y = x$. From (2.4) this gives x_1. Repetition of the procedure gives $x_2, x_3, \ldots$ in succession. It is easy to see whether

† J. M. Hyslop, *Real Variable*, Oliver and Boyd (1960), § 6.2.

the procedure converges or not. From the diagrams in Fig. 2.1 it is clear that convergence to the required root can occur only in cases (a) and (b), namely when $|F'(x)| < 1$ and the first approximation is sufficiently near the required root.

Even if there are mistakes in the intermediate steps the above iterative procedure will give the correct final answer provided that the iteration ultimately converges to the required root (cf. Ex. 2.14). On the other hand mistakes may delay convergence or cause convergence to another root. One simple check that should be applied mentally in hand computation is that, as the calculation proceeds, the x_r tend to a limiting value monotonically as in the case of Fig. 2.1(a), or they lie alternately on either side of a limiting value as in the case of Fig. 2.1(b).

We now return to consideration of the iterative procedure (2.2) for which $F(x) = 0.2x^2 + 0.4$, $F'(x) = 0.4x$. There are two roots $\alpha \approx 0.44$ and $\beta \approx 4.6$ so that $|F'(\alpha)| < 1$ and $|F'(\beta)| > 1$. Hence the above theory tells us that if we try iterating with an initial approximation near α the procedure will converge to this root but if we start with an initial approximation near β the procedure will not converge to β. The iteration can be examined graphically as in Fig. 2.2(a). Proceeding as for Fig. 2.1. it can be shown that if we choose an initial approximation x_0 such that $|x_0| < \beta$ then the iterative procedure will converge to the smaller root α, but if $|x_0| > \beta$ the procedure will diverge.

There are of course a large number of ways in which we can rearrange an equation $f(x) = 0$ in the form $x = F(x)$ and each rearrangement will give an iterative procedure of type (2.4) with, in general, different convergence properties. Thus if we rearrange (2.1) in the form $x = 5 - (2/x)$ we have the iterative formula

$$x_{r+1} = 5 - \frac{2}{x_r}.$$

In this case $F'(x) = 2/x^2$ so that $|F'(\alpha)| > 1$, $|F'(\beta)| < 1$, and the procedure will converge to the larger root β if we start with an initial approximation near the larger root but it will not converge to the smaller root α if we start with an approximation near to α. The situation is illustrated in

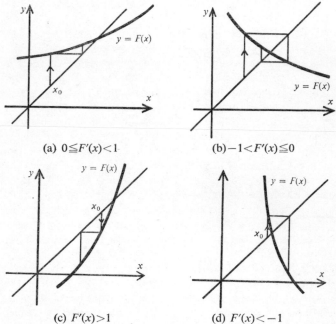

(a) $0 \leqq F'(x) < 1$ (b) $-1 < F'(x) \leqq 0$

(c) $F'(x) > 1$ (d) $F'(x) < -1$

FIG. 2.1   Diagrams illustrating the iterative procedure $x_{r+1} = F(x_r)$

Fig. 2.2(b) from which it is clear that the procedure ultimately converges to the larger root whatever first approximation x_0 is chosen.

Still another example is illustrated in Fig. 2.2(c) which shows the iterative solution of the trivial equation $x = -x^3$. The procedure converges to the root $x = 0$ if we choose $|x_0| < 1$, but diverges if we choose $|x_0| > 1$.

The discussion given above has illustrated the following points in connection with iterative procedures:

(i) If we wish to obtain a specific root of an equation it may be necessary to try various iterative methods obtained by rearranging the equation $f(x) = 0$ in the form $x = F(x)$ in different ways until we obtain a sequence which converges to the required root.

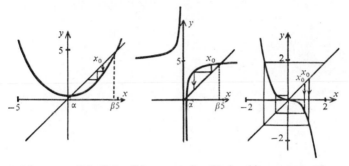

(a) $x_{r+1} = 0 \cdot 2x_r^2 \cdot 0 \cdot 4$ (b) $x_{r+1} = 5 - (2/x_r)$ (c) $x_{r+1} = -x_r^3$

FIG. 2.2   Examples of the iterative procedure $x_{r+1} = F(x_r)$

(ii) It is important from a practical point of view that convergence should be as rapid as possible. For rapid convergence of the procedure (2.4) discussed in this section it is clear from (2.8) that $|F'(x)|$ should be as small as possible, and x_0 should be chosen as near to the required root as possible.

(iii) In considering whether an iteration is converging or not it may be necessary to ignore the first few iterations since the procedure may appear to diverge initially, even though it ultimately converges.

(iv) In the iterative procedure considered in this section the correct final answer is obtained even though there are mistakes in the intermediate steps, provided that the iteration ultimately converges to the desired root.

The rate of convergence of iterative methods of the type discussed in this section tends to be rather slow, and in practice a device is used to accelerate the convergence, as discussed in § 2.4 below.

§ **2.3. The Newton-Raphson iterative method.** Let X be an approximate root of $f(x) = 0$ and suppose that the exact root is $x = X + h$, so that h is a small quantity. Then $f(X+h) = 0$ and, expanding by Taylor's theorem, we have

$$f(X+h) = 0 = f(X) + hf'(X) + \tfrac{1}{2}h^2 f''(X) + \dots \quad (2.9)$$

If h is small and $f(x)$ is a well behaved function in the neighbourhood of the required root, the terms in h^2, h^3, ... can be neglected, so that

$$h \approx -f(X)/f'(X).$$

The **Newton-Raphson iterative formula** is obtained by writing this result as an iterative procedure:

$$x_{r+1} = x_r - \frac{f(x_r)}{f'(x_r)}, \quad (2.10)$$

where, as in § 2.2, we start with an estimate x_0 and calculate in succession $x_1, x_2, \dots$.

The geometrical interpretation of the Newton-Raphson method can be seen from Fig. 2.3(a). Suppose that the curve $f(x) = 0$ cuts the x-axis at A, so that $OA = x$. If $x_r = OC$, then $CD = f(x_r)$ and $\tan C\hat{B}D = f'(x_r)$. Also $BC = CD \cot C\hat{B}D$. Hence

$$OB = OC - BC = x_r - f(x_r)/f'(x_r),$$

so that $OB = x_{r+1}$, from (2.10). The diagram indicates that once the procedure starts to converge towards a root, it will converge from one side. Under exceptional circumstances this may not be true, for instance if $f'' = 0$, $(f'''/f') < 0$ at the root. Also the first few iterates may oscillate on either side of a root, as in Fig. 2.3(b).

Difficulties may arise if $f'(x) = 0$ near a root of $f(x) = 0$ which it is required to determine, particularly when the equation has two nearly equal roots in this region. These difficulties can often be clarified by plotting the curve

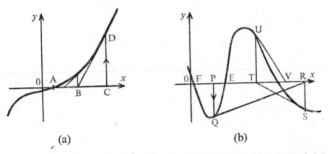

(a)   (b)

FIG. 2.3   Convergence of the Newton-Raphson iterative procedure

$y = f(x)$ for values of x near the required root and examining the geometrical interpretation of the Newton-Raphson procedure. Thus in Fig. 2.3(b) if we start from the abscissa P we certainly do not converge to either of the roots at E, F though of course the procedure converges to another root of the equation. It is usually sufficient to ensure that the x_r approach the required root of the equation from the side opposite to that on which $f'(x) = 0$. If $f'(x)$ is small near the required zero of $f(x) = 0$ then it may be necessary to compute $f(x_r)$ and $f'(x_r)$ to a high degree of accuracy in order to obtain an accurate estimate of x_{r+1}. This indicates that the equation is " ill-conditioned ". The meanings of the words " ill-conditioned " and " accurate " are discussed in connection with polynomials in § 2.6.

To examine the rate of convergence of the Newton-Raphson method we use the results in § 2.2, (2.4)-(2.6). To apply these to the present case we must set

$$F(x) = x - f(x)/f'(x),$$

so that

$$F'(x) = f(x)f''(x)/\{f'(x)\}^2 = 0,$$

$$F''(x) = f''(x)/f'(x) \neq 0, \text{ in general,}$$

where in both equations we have used the fact that $f(x) = 0$. Hence from (2.6a), since $\delta x_r = x - x_r$,

$$x - x_{r+1} = -\tfrac{1}{2}p(x - x_r)^2 + \ldots, \text{ where } p = f''/f'. \quad (2.11)$$

If x_r is nearly equal to the required root x, the higher order terms can be neglected and the error in x_{r+1} is proportional to the *square* of the error in x_r. This means that the rate of convergence of the Newton-Raphson procedure is very much more rapid than the rate of convergence of the simple iterative method discussed in § 2.2. This is illustrated in the following examples where the final estimate of x is obtained by repeating the iteration until x_{r+1} and x_r agree. Care may have to be exercised when using this criterion when working to a fixed number of decimal places, as discussed in § 2.6 below. Some general aspects of rates of convergence, including estimation of the rate of convergence, are discussed in the next section.

Ex. 2.1. *Find the roots of $x^2 - 5x + 2 = 0$ to five decimal places by the Newton-Raphson procedure.*

If we choose $f(x) = x^2 - 5x + 2$ then (2.10) gives

$$x_{r+1} = \frac{x_r^2 - 2}{2x_r - 5}.$$

On taking $x_0 = 0$ we find $x_1 = 0\cdot4$ and $x_2 = 0\cdot438\,095$, $x_3 = 0\cdot438\,447$, $x_4 = 0\cdot438\,447$. The extremely rapid convergence is evident. (Compare results (2.3) from the procedure in § 2.2.) On starting from $x_0 = 4 \cdot 0$ we find $x_1 = 14/3$ and $x_2 = 4 \cdot 564\ 104$, $x_3 = 4 \cdot 561\ 554$, $x_4 = x_5 = 4 \cdot 561\ 553$. In this example it is convenient to work to six decimal places throughout. In calculating x_2 it would have been sufficient to have worked to three decimal places, but we did not know this beforehand. In more complicated examples it may be convenient to work to a small number of decimal places in the earlier iterations until the procedure starts to converge rapidly.

When using the Newton-Raphson procedure it may not be necessary to recompute $f'(x)$ at each iteration. It may be sufficient to use an approximate value of $f'(x)$. Thus in the above example we can write

$$x_{r+1} = x_r - \frac{x_r^2 - 5x_r + 2}{(2x_r - 5)^*},$$

where the star denotes an approximate value. On choosing $x_0 = 0$ we find $x_1 = 0 \cdot 4$. To obtain a simple formula we set $(2x_r - 5)^* = -4$ and use the iteration

$$x_{r+1} = x_r + \tfrac{1}{4}(x_r^2 - 5x_r + 2) = \tfrac{1}{4}(x_r^2 - x_r + 2).$$

With $x_1 = 0 \cdot 4$ this gives

$$x_2 = 0 \cdot 44, \qquad x_3 = 0 \cdot 4384, \qquad x_4 = 0 \cdot 483\ 449.$$

These figures should be compared with those obtained previously. Although the rate of convergence is of course not so rapid as in the true second-order procedure, it is still remarkably good considering the crudeness of the approximation used for $2x_r - 5$. Although we have approximated to $f'(x)$ it is essential to calculate $f(x)$ to full accuracy. It often happens in iterative processes that we can be relatively crude in certain parts of the calculation, but accuracy must be maintained in certain vital parts of the calculation.

Ex. 2.2. *Find* $\sqrt{11}$ *to five decimal places by an iterative procedure.*

We wish to solve the equation $x^2 = a$. On writing $f(x) = x^2 - a$ the Newton-Raphson formula gives

$$x_{r+1} = x_r - \tfrac{1}{2}\left(x_r - \frac{a}{x_r}\right) = \tfrac{1}{2}\left(x_r + \frac{a}{x_r}\right)$$

where the first form is convenient for hand computation since $x_r - (a/x_r)$ is a small quantity. If we choose $x_0 = 3$ then

$$x_1 = 3 \cdot 33, \qquad x_2 = 3 \cdot 316\ 65, \qquad x_3 = 3 \cdot 316\ 62,$$

where x_3 is correct to five decimals. This is a very convenient method for finding square roots on a desk calculator.

Ex. 2.3. *Solve* $x = \exp(1/x)$ *to five decimal places.*

Various formulae can be obtained for the iteration by rearranging the equation in different ways. If we choose $f(x) = x - \exp(1/x)$ the Newton-Raphson formula gives

$$x_{r+1} = x_r - x_r^2\{x_r - \exp(1/x_r)\}/\{x_r^2 + \exp(1/x_r)\}. \tag{i}$$

If we write $x = 1/y$ so that $f(y) = 1 - y \exp y$, we find

$$y_{r+1} = y_r + \{\exp(-y_r) - y_r\}/(1 + y_r). \tag{ii}$$

If we take logarithms and write $f(x) = 1 - x \ln x$, then

$$x_{r+1} = x_r + (1 - x_r \ln x_r)/(1 + \ln x_r). \tag{iii}$$

Forms (ii) and (iii) are more convenient than (i).

It is found graphically that there is only one root near $x = 1 \cdot 8$ (or $y = 0 \cdot 6$). With initial approximation $y_0 = 0 \cdot 6$ formula (ii) gives successively $0 \cdot 568$, $0 \cdot 567\ 144$ i.e. $x = 1 \cdot 763\ 22$. With initial approximation $x = 1 \cdot 8$ formula (iii) gives successively $1 \cdot 7634$, $1 \cdot 763\ 22$. The final iteration should of course be repeated as a check.

§ **2.4. General aspects of iterative procedures.** If an
iterative procedure for finding a quantity x by calculating
successively x_1, x_2, ... is such that

$$x - x_{r+1} = a_k(x - x_r)^k + a_{k+1}(x - x_r)^{k+1} + ... \quad (2.12)$$

where a_k is a non-zero constant, we say that the iterative
process is of the **kth-order**. We see from (2.6b) that the
simple procedure in § 2.2 gives in general a first-order
process, and from (2.11) that the Newton-Raphson
procedure is second order.

The order of the iterative procedure $x_{r+1} = F(x_r)$ for
finding a root x can be obtained by expanding $F(x_r)$ in a
Taylor series around x, as in (2.6a). If the first non-zero
derivative of $F(x)$ is of the kth order then the iterative
procedure is also of the kth order, since (2.12) and (2.6a)
then agree, with $k!a_k = (-1)^{k+1}F^{(k)}(x)$. If $F(x)$ has a
simple form it may be easy to determine the order of an
iterative procedure by finding the order of the first non-
vanishing derivative, as in the following example. If $F(x)$ is
complicated it may be simpler to obtain the expansion
(2.12) directly, as in the argument leading to (2.17) below.

Ex. 2.4. *Show that* $x_{r+1} = x_r(3 - 3ax_r + a^2x_r^2)$ *is a third-
order process for the calculation of* $1/a$.
We have

$$F(x) = 3x - 3ax^2 + a^2x^3, \quad F'(x) = 3(ax-1)^2,$$

$$F''(x) = 6a(ax-1), \quad F'''(x) = 6a^2.$$

The equation $x = F(x)$ has three roots, namely $x = 0$,
$1/a$, $2/a$. If $x = 0$ the process is first-order with $F'(x) = 3 > 1$,
and therefore the iteration will never converge to $x = 0$.
Similarly if $x = 2/a$ the process is first-order with
$F'(x) = 3 > 1$ and the iteration will not converge to $x = 2/a$.
The remaining possibility is $x = 1/a$ and then $F'(x) = F''(x)$
$= 0$, $F'''(x) \neq 0$, so that we have a third-order process for
the calculation of $1/a$.

We shall use the following notation for the approximate relations between the errors in x_r and x_{r+1} for first- and second-order procedures, respectively:

$$x - x_{r+1} = M(x - x_r), \qquad (2.13)$$

$$x - x_{r+1} = N(x - x_r)^2. \qquad (2.14)$$

A second-order process is extremely rapidly convergent once the error becomes small enough. If the error at any stage of an iteration is δ, the error in successive iterates in a second-order process is

$$N\delta^2, \quad N^3\delta^4, \quad N^7\delta^8, \quad \dots \quad N^{-1}(N\delta)^{2^r}, \quad \dots .$$

Hence the procedure is convergent if $|N\delta| < 1$, and the smaller $|N\delta|$ is, the more rapid the convergence. The term $|N\delta|^{2^r}$ ultimately goes to zero extremely rapidly as r increases, for any value of $|N\delta|$ less than unity. If $N\delta = 0\cdot1$, then the sequence $(N\delta)^2$, $(N\delta)^4$, $(N\delta)^8$, ... gives $0\cdot01$, $0\cdot0001$, $0\cdot000\,000\,01$, ... If $N\delta = 0\cdot9$ we have, approximately, the sequence $0\cdot81$, $0\cdot656$, $0\cdot430$, $0\cdot185$, $0\cdot054$, $0\cdot0029$, $0\cdot000\,008\,4$, ... The convergence is initially slow but ultimately rapid. Once the state of rapid convergence is reached, each iteration will roughly double the number of correct figures in the answer, but it is misleading to state without qualification that second-order processes double the number of significant figures per iteration. For instance the iteration may be started with a value of x_0 so far from the required root that the second-order analysis may not apply to the first few iterations. In this case the initial convergence may be very slow. In fact one of the problems in applying second-order processes is to arrange that the state of rapid convergence is reached after as few iterations as possible (compare Ex. 3.1, Program 3.5).

In first-order processes the behaviour of the error is completely different from that just discussed in connection with second-order processes. If the initial error is δ, the errors in a first-order process are successively

$$M\delta, \quad M^2\delta, \quad M^3\delta, \quad \dots \quad M^r\delta, \quad \dots \;.$$

The error is reduced by a constant factor M in each iteration. This means that there is no ultimate extremely rapid convergence as in second-order processes.

Because of the comparatively slow convergence of first-order processes it is often desirable to improve the rate of convergence by the following important method. From (2.13) we assume that, for the first-order procedure under consideration,

$$X - x_r = M(X - x_{r-1}),$$

$$X - x_{r-1} = M(X - x_{r-2}),$$

where X is an approximation to the root. On eliminating M and rearranging we obtain an expression for X in terms of x_r, x_{r-1}, x_{r-2} which will be, in general, a better approximation to the root than any of the iterates. We find

$$
\begin{aligned}
X &= \frac{x_r x_{r-2} - x_{r-1}^2}{x_r - 2x_{r-1} + x_{r-2}} \\
&= x_r - \frac{(x_r - x_{r-1})^2}{x_r - 2x_{r-1} + x_{r-2}},
\end{aligned}
\tag{2.15}
$$

where the second form is more convenient for calculation (compare Ex. 1.2). The use of (2.15) is usually called **Aitken's δ^2-process** since A. C. Aitken popularised its applications in numerical analysis. It goes back at least as far as Kummer in 1837. As an example consider the figures (2.3):

$$x_2 = 0{\cdot}432, \quad x_3 = 0{\cdot}437\,32, \quad x_4 = 0{\cdot}438\,25. \tag{2.16a}$$

Substitution in (2.15) gives

$$X = 0{\cdot}438\,25 - (0{\cdot}000\,93)^2/(-0{\cdot}004\,39) = 0{\cdot}438\,45. \tag{2.16b}$$

If we use this value as a new x_0 in (2.2) and start a new sequence of iterations we find that the first iterate repeats the value 0·438 45 so that the iteration converges to this estimate of the root.

(It is convenient at this point to anticipate notation introduced in § 7.2 in order to explain the name " δ^2-process ". Suppose that the numbers (2.16a) are arranged in a difference table:

	x_i	δ	δ^2
x_{r-2}	0·432 00		
		532	
x_{r-1}	0·437 32		-439
		93	
x_r	0·438 25		

The quantity $x_r - x_{r-1}$ (= 93) is the first difference $\delta x_{r-\frac{1}{2}}$, and $x_r - 2x_{r-1} + x_{r-2}$ (= -439) is the second difference $\delta^2 x_{r-1}$, in units of the fifth decimal place. These numbers occur in (2.16b) above. The name " δ^2-process " comes from this connection with differences.)

This type of procedure, namely using several successive iterates to obtain an improved estimate of the root, which is then used as an initial approximation for a further sequence of iterations is called **accelerating the convergence**. It must be remembered that in the derivation of formulae for accelerating convergence we assume that round-off errors are negligible. The formulae will not be valid if round-off errors are comparable with the differences between successive iterates. Although we stated at the end of § 2.2 that mistakes are usually not very important in iterative procedures this is obviously no longer true when accelerating procedures are used. An accelerating procedure may make convergence worse if the assumptions on which the procedure are based are not satisfied. Thus Aitken's δ^2-process is based on (2.13) which assumes a first-order procedure. Consider the following figures from Ex. 2.1 illustrating the Newton-Raphson second-order procedure:

$$x_1 = 4 \cdot 666\ 667, \quad x_2 = 4 \cdot 564\ 104, \quad x_3 = 4 \cdot 561\ 554.$$

The δ^2-process indicates that x_3 is in error by $0 \cdot 000\ 065$ whereas the error is in fact only $0 \cdot 000\ 001$.

To examine the convergence of Aitken's process, suppose that a first-order procedure gives three successive iterates x_0, x_1, x_2 which are used to obtain a new initial value $x_0^{(1)}$ by means of (2.15). From $x_0^{(1)}$ we deduce $x_1^{(1)}$, $x_2^{(1)}$ by the first-order procedure and then use (2.15) to obtain $x_0^{(2)}$, and so on. From the definition of a first-order procedure we have

$$x - x_1 = a_1(x - x_0) + a_2(x - x_0)^2 + \dots ,$$
$$x - x_2 = a_1(x - x_1) + a_2(x - x_1)^2 + \dots$$
$$= a_1^2(x - x_0) + a_1 a_2(1 + a_1)(x - x_0)^2 + \dots,$$

where a_1, a_2 are constants. Hence

$$x_2 - 2x_1 + x_0$$
$$= -(1 - a_1)^2(x - x_0) + a_2(2 - a_1 - a_1^2)(x - x_0)^2 + \dots,$$

$$(x_2 - x_1)^2$$
$$= a_1^2(1 - a_1)^2(x - x_0)^2 + 2a_1 a_2(1 - 2a_1 - a_1^3)(x - x_0)^3 + \dots .$$

On substituting these results in (2.15) with $r = 2$ we find

$$x - x_0^{(1)} = C(x - x_0)^2, \tag{2.17}$$

where C is a constant. Similarly, in general,

$$x - x_0^{(r+1)} = C(x - x_0^{(r)})^2,$$

so that Aitken's δ^2-process for accelerating convergence is second-order.

The question of whether to use a first-order process with

acceleration of convergence, or the Newton-Raphson second-order process, depends on the particular equation considered. As a broad generalisation, if $f'(x)$ has a simple form then the Newton-Raphson procedure will be preferable but in complicated examples the accelerated first-order procedure may be simpler. Second-order processes are so quickly convergent that it is seldom necessary to consider third- or higher-order processes, although procedures of arbitrarily high order can be constructed for any given iterative problem.

When using a first-order iterative procedure it is often useful to estimate the quantity M in (2.13), after each iteration. By subtracting the equations

$$x - x_r = M(x - x_{r-1}), \quad x - x_{r-1} = M(x - x_{r-2}),$$

we find

$$M = \frac{x_r - x_{r-1}}{x_{r-1} - x_{r-2}} = \frac{1}{t}, \qquad (2.18a)$$

say, where t, the reciprocal of M, has been introduced since it is usually more convenient to work in terms of t rather than M. By inspection we see that equation (2.15) for the δ^2-process can be written in terms of t as

$$X = x_r + \frac{1}{t-1}(x_r - x_{r-1}). \qquad (2.18b)$$

As an example the figures in (2.16a) give

$$t = 532/93 \approx 6,$$
$$X = 0.438\ 25 + \tfrac{1}{5}(0.000\ 93) = 0.4384_4.$$

From (2.6) we see that, when solving the equation $x = F(x)$, the theoretical value of M is $F'(x)$. In this example the theoretical value of t is therefore $t = 1/M = 1/(0.4x) \approx 6$. However in practice it is useful to compute the empirical value of t after each iteration since if the successive estimates of t tend to a constant value this confirms that δ^2-extrapolation will be valid.

In a similar way when using a second-order procedure it is useful to estimate N in (2.14) after each iteration. Since a second-order procedure converges very rapidly we estimate N by replacing x by x_r in the equation

$$x - x_{r-1} = N(x - x_{r-2})^2.$$

This gives

$$N \approx (x_r - x_{r-1})/(x_r - x_{r-2})^2. \qquad (2.18c)$$

Similarly to estimate x we assume that we can replace x by x_r on the right of the following equation:

$$x - x_r = N(x - x_{r-1})^2.$$

This gives

$$x = x_r + N(x_r - x_{r-1})^2, \qquad (2.18d)$$

where it will be assumed that the value of N is estimated by means of (2.18c). In terms of the quantity t defined in (2.18a) this formula becomes

$$x = x_r + \frac{1}{(t+1)^2}(x_r - x_{r-1}), \qquad (2.18e)$$

though now t will not tend to a constant value independent of r as r increases. As a numerical example consider the following figures from Ex. 2.1:

$$x_1 = 4\cdot666\ 667, \quad x_2 = 4\cdot564\ 104, \quad x_3 = 4\cdot561\ 554.$$

Then

$$N \approx 0\cdot0025/(0\cdot1)^2 = \tfrac{1}{4},$$

$$x - x_4 \approx \tfrac{1}{4}(0\cdot0025)^2 = 0\cdot000\ 001\ 6,$$

which indicates that x_1 should be correct to within about two digits in the sixth decimal place. Alternatively we

D

calculate

$$t = 0\cdot1/0\cdot0025 = 40,$$

$$x - x_4 \approx 0\cdot0025/41^2 = 0\cdot000\ 001\ 6,$$

as before. The above formulae should not be applied until the iterative procedure has started to converge systematically.

§ **2.5. Real roots of polynomials.** The general polynomial equation of degree n is (assuming $a_0 \neq 0$):

$$P_n(x) = a_0x^n + a_1x^{n-1} + \ldots + a_n = 0. \qquad (2.19)$$

The following properties of polynomial equations should be borne in mind[†]:

(i) A polynomial equation of degree n has exactly n roots. (A factor $(x-a)^m$ gives a repeated root which must be counted m times.)

(ii) If the equation has real coefficients, complex roots occur in pairs. If $p+iq$ is a root then $p-iq$ is a root. An equation of odd order has at least one real root.

(iii) If the roots are $x_1, x_2, \ldots x_n$ then

$$x_1 + x_2 + \ldots + x_n = -(a_1/a_0),$$

$$x_1x_2\ldots x_n = (-1)^n(a_n/a_0),$$

$$\sum x_1x_2\ldots x_r = (-1)^r(a_r/a_0), \quad r = 2 \text{ to } n-1.$$

In this equation the sum is taken over all possible products of r distinct x_i chosen from the n roots.

(iv) If one root is much smaller than the others then it is given approximately by $a_{n-1}x + a_n = 0$. Similarly the two smallest roots are often given

[†] H. W. Turnbull, *Theory of Equations*, 5th Edition (Oliver and Boyd, 1957).

approximately by the roots of $a_{n-2}x^2 + a_{n-1}x + a_n = 0$. If one root is much larger than the other it is given approximately by $a_0 x + a_1 = 0$. The two largest roots are often given approximately by $a_0 x^2 + a_1 x + a_2 = 0$.

The Newton-Raphson formula can be applied to the polynomial equation (2.19). If u is an approximate root of this equation then an improved root is given by

$$u - \{P_n(u)/P_n'(u)\}. \qquad (2.20)$$

It is desirable to systematise the calculation of $P_n(u)/P_n'(u)$. We consider only real u. Suppose that division of $P_n(x)$ by $x - u$ gives

$$P_n(x) = (x-u)Q_{n-1}(x) + B.$$

Then

$$P_n(u) = B.$$

Also

$$P_n'(x) = Q_{n-1}(x) + (x-u)Q_{n-1}'(x).$$

Hence

$$P_n'(u) = Q_{n-1}(u).$$

Suppose that division of $Q_{n-1}(x)$ by $x-u$ gives

$$Q_{n-1}(x) = (x-u)R_{n-2}(x) + D.$$

Then

$$P_n'(u) = Q_{n-1}(u) = D.$$

From (2.20) the improved value of u is therefore given by

$$u - B/D.$$

The calculation of B by long-hand division, which also

gives the coefficients of $Q_{n-1}(x)$, proceeds as follows:

$$
\begin{array}{llllllllll}
x-u) & a_0 & & a_1 & & a_2 & a_3 & \dots & (b_0 & b_1 & b_2 \\
& b_0 & & -b_0 u & & & & & \\
\hline
& & b_1 & & & a_2 & \\
& & b_1 & & & -b_1 u & \\
\hline
& & & b_2 & & a_3 & \dots
\end{array}
$$

where $b_0 = a_0$, $b_1 = a_1 + b_0 u$, $b_2 = a_2 + b_1 u$, etc. The evaluation of B is essentially the evaluation of the polynomial $P_n(u)$ by nested multiplication:

$$P_n(u) = [\{(a_0 u + a_1)u + a_2\}u + a_3]u + \dots,$$

mentioned in Ex. 1.4. It is convenient to tabulate the calculation in the form given below, where $b_n = B = P_n(u)$. We include also the calculation required for $P_n'(u) = D$ given by c_{n-1} in the table

$$
\begin{array}{ccccccc}
a_0 & a_1 & a_2 & a_3 & \dots & a_{n-1} & a_n \\
& b_0 u & b_1 u & b_2 u & & b_{n-2}u & b_{n-1}u \\
\hline
b_0 & b_1 & b_2 & b_3 & & b_{n-1} & b_n \\
& c_0 u & c_1 u & c_2 u & & c_{n-2}u & \\
\hline
c_0 & c_1 & c_2 & c_3 & & c_{n-1} &
\end{array}
\quad (2.21)
$$

The sequence is to calculate in succession b_0, $b_0 u$, b_1, $b_1 u$, b_2, etc. When the student has gained some practice it will be possible to form $b_r = a_r + b_{r-1}u$ in one machine operation without recording $b_{r-1}u$, and similarly for c_r, so that the second and fourth rows can be omitted in the above table.

If several roots are required the roots should be determined in the order of increasing absolute value, and it is usually satisfactory (and desirable) to remove them from the polynomial as they are determined. (See Ex. 3.3 where this procedure is discussed in connection with automatic computing.) The polynomial obtained by dividing $P_n(x)$

by $x - u$ is

$$P_{n-1}(x) = b_0 x^{n-1} + b_1 x^{n-2} + \ldots + b_{n-1},$$

so that the coefficients of $P_{n-1}(x)$ have been determined in the course of the Newton-Raphson procedure for finding the roots of $P_n(x)$.

Ex. 2.5. *Find the real root of the following equation to four decimal places.*

$$x^5 + 2 \cdot 653 x^4 + 4 \cdot 512 x^3 - 2 \cdot 043 x^2 - 0 \cdot 263 x - 0 \cdot 251 = 0.$$

A graph shows that the real root is near $0 \cdot 5$ and we take this as x_0. The procedure leading to the table (2.21), without the second and fourth rows, gives, on using five decimal places throughout for convenience:

1	2·653 00	4·512 00	−2·043 00	−0·263 00	−0·251 00 (0·5
1	3·153 00	6·088 50	1·001 25	0·237 62	−0·132 19
1	3·653 00	7·915 00	4·958 75	2·717 00	

1	2·653 00	4·512 00	−2·043 00	−0·263 00	−0·251 00 (0·549
1	3·202 00	6·269 90	1·399 18	0·505 15	0·026 33
1	3·751 00	8·329 20	5·971 91	3·783 73	

The first correction is $\delta_1 = 0 \cdot 132\ 19 / 2 \cdot 717\ 00 = 0 \cdot 049$, giving $x_1 = 0 \cdot 549$. The second correction is $\delta_2 = -0 \cdot 026\ 33 / 3 \cdot 783\ 73 = -0 \cdot 006\ 96$ giving $x_2 = 0 \cdot 5420_4$. A further iteration gives a final value of $0 \cdot 5419$, correct to four decimal places.

§ **2.6. Errors when finding roots of polynomials.** When we wish to specify the accuracy of an approximation X to a root x of an equation $f(x) = 0$ there are at least three different ways in which the word "accuracy" can be interpreted:

    (i) Assuming that $f(x)$ is specified exactly then $|X - x|$ is the absolute accuracy of X and $|X - x| / |x|$

is the relative accuracy of X. We shall normally use the word " accuracy " in one of these senses.

(ii) If we do not know x then the smallness of the quantity $f(X) = R$, say, gives some indication of the accuracy of X. The quantity R is called the **residual**. It is most important to realise that small R does not necessarily mean that the absolute or relative error of X is small. This is discussed below.

(iii) If the constants defining the equation $f(x) = 0$ (for example the coefficients, if $f(x)$ is a polynomial) are not known exactly, then the uncertainty in these constants means that there is an uncertainty in the values of the roots of $f(x) = 0$. The accuracy of an approximate root can be no greater than the uncertainty produced in the roots by possible variations in the constants defining the equation.

In some cases, with reference to (ii), small values of R can be produced by values of X appreciably different from the exact roots; and with reference to (iii) small variations in constants can produce large variations in the roots. These phenomena often appear together. In either case the equations are said to be **ill-conditioned**. As an example consider the equation

$$f(x) = x^2 - 1 \cdot 064x + 0 \cdot 283 = 0, \qquad (2.22)$$

which has roots $0 \cdot 527$, $0 \cdot 537$ to three decimal places. The equation

$$x^2 - 1 \cdot 0641x + 0 \cdot 283 = 0$$

has roots $0 \cdot 523$, $0 \cdot 541$; changing a coefficient by 1 in 10,000 has changed the roots by 1 in 130. If we substitute $x = 0 \cdot 532$ in (2.22) then $f(x) = R = -0 \cdot 000\,024$; changing x by 1 in 100 produces a residual which is one ten-thousandth of the smallest coefficient. It should be emphasised that these phenomena are inherent in the equation; they appear whatever method is used to solve the equation.

Since in the above example a change of 0·001 in a root produces a change of only 0·000 005 in R, we need to work to six decimal places in order to verify that a root is accurate to three decimals. To examine the reason for this more closely, we note that in the Newton-Raphson method the correction to the root is $-f(x)/f'(x)$. In the above example, although $f(x) = R$ is small, $f'(x)$ is also small. For example, if we choose $x = 0·525$,

$$f(x) = (0·525)^2 - 1·064(0·525) + 0·283 = 0·000 025,$$

$$f'(x) = 2(0·525) - 1·064 = 0·014.$$

We encounter the familiar difficulty that in computing $f(x)$ and $f'(x)$, the cancellation of large numbers gives small numbers, and in order to obtain a moderate degree of accuracy for their quotient we need to work to a large number of decimal places. This is not a criticism of Newton's method. The difficulty will occur in one form or another, whatever method is used to solve the equation.

To illustrate by a numerical example, consider the formula obtained by applying the Newton-Raphson formula (2.10) to (2.22):

$$x_{r+1} = \frac{x_r^2 - 0·283}{2x_r - 1·064}.$$

Iteration with $x_0 = 0·55$, working to four decimal places, gives

$$x_1 = \frac{0·0195}{0·0360} = 0·5417, \quad x_2 = \frac{0·0104}{0·0194} = 0·5361, \quad (2.23)$$

and then in succession 0·5366, 0·5326, 0·5833, 0·5575, 0·5451, 0·5382, 0·5403, 0·5361, ... This last number, which is x_{10}, is in fact identical with x_2 and further iteration will merely repeat the values for x_3 to x_{10}. Even though we have used four decimal places, all we can say about the root is that it is near $0 \cdot 54$. Equation (2.23) shows clearly the way in which significant figures are lost in intermediate calculations. Similarly if five decimals are used in the calculation it will be found that the iterates vary between $0 \cdot 536\ 50$ and $0 \cdot 537\ 50$ in general, and we can say that the root is approximately $0 \cdot 537$. There is no guarantee that the correct answer lies between the upper and lower limits within which the iterates fluctuate, or even that if an iteration apparently converges that it converges to the correct answer. Thus in the above example if we iterate with $x_0 = 0 \cdot 50$ using four decimal places, we find in succession $0 \cdot 5156$, $0 \cdot 5244$, $0 \cdot 5263$ and all further iterations repeat $0 \cdot 5263$, but we know that the correct answer in this case is $0 \cdot 5270$.

To sum up this discussion: in order to calculate any root to a specified degree of accuracy an essential and unavoidable degree of accuracy is necessary in the intermediate calculations and this may be much greater than the final accuracy of the root.

The change δx in a root x produced by a change δa_r in a coefficient a_r can be examined theoretically as follows. The quantity $x + \delta x$ is a root of the perturbed equation, so that

$$P_n(x + \delta x) + \delta a_r(x + \delta x)^{n-r} = 0,$$

Hence to first order, since $P_n(x) = 0$,

$$P_n'(x)\delta x + \delta a_r x^{n-r} = 0,$$

or

$$\delta x = -\delta a_r\{x^{n-r}/P_n'(x)\}. \tag{2.24}$$

When $\{x^{n-r}/P_n'(x)\}$ is large for any root, then by our previous definition this root is ill-conditioned. Of course the linear approximation on the basis of which (2.24) is derived breaks down for ill-conditioned roots. Equation (2.24) is not quantitatively accurate for the polynomial (2.22), for example, but the qualitative indication of ill-conditioning is correct. Formula (2.24) indicates that the smaller roots tend to be better conditioned than the larger roots since, if x_i is the ith root, the power x_i^{n-r} usually increases more rapidly with i than $P_n'(x_i)$.

Some instructive illustrations of the application of (2.24) are given by J. H. Wilkinson† from whose paper the following examples are quoted. In this paragraph we assume that x_1, x_2, ... x_n represent the n roots of a polynomial of degree n. (Elsewhere in this chapter x_r denotes the rth approximation to a root in an iterative procedure.) If we consider the polynomial equation

$$P_{20}(x) = (x+1)(x+2)...(x+20) = 0, \qquad (2.25)$$

with roots $x_s = -s$, ($s = 1$ to 20), we find for a change δa_1 in a_1:

$$\delta x_{20} \approx 0{\cdot}4 \times 10^8 \delta a_1, \ \delta x_{15} \approx 0{\cdot}2 \times 10^{10} \delta a_1, \ \delta x_5 \approx 0{\cdot}6 \delta a_1.$$

The roots x_1 to x_5 are well-conditioned, but the conditioning is extremely poor for the large roots. If we consider the polynomial equation

$$(x+1)(x+2)...(x+20)+2^{-23}x^{19} = 0,$$

which differs from (2·25) by about 10^{-7} in a_1, the roots are $x_s = -s$ to nine decimal places for $s = 1$ to 4, but x_{10}, x_{11} are $-10{\cdot}10 \pm 0{\cdot}64i$, x_{15}, x_{16} are $-13{\cdot}99 \pm 2{\cdot}52i$, and x_{19}, x_{20} are $-19{\cdot}50 \pm 1{\cdot}94i$. Among other things, this example illustrates in a remarkable way that some roots can be ill-conditioned and others well-conditioned, in the same equation.

Although it is true that ill-conditioning is usually

† *The evaluation of the zeros of ill-conditioned polynomials*, Numerische Mathematik, **1** (1959), 150-180. This excellent paper will repay careful study.

associated with the occurrence of nearly equal roots, which in turn implies that $f'(x)$ is small, this remark should be interpreted with care. Thus the equation

$$x^{20} + 1 = 0,$$

which has 20 roots, all of modulus unity, is comparatively well-conditioned. This can be confirmed by using (2.24).

§ 2.7. Bairstow's method for finding complex roots of polynomials.

In this section we extend the Newton-Raphson method for real roots (§ 2.5) to give formulae convenient for dealing with complex roots. Suppose that w is an approximate complex root of $P_n(x) = 0$, where the polynomial has real coefficients. Consider the quadratic factor $(x-w)(x-\overline{w}) = x^2 - px - q$, say, where $\overline{w}$ is the complex conjugate of w, so that p, q are real. We write (cf. (2.19), (2.20))

$$P_n(x) = (x^2 - px - q)S_{n-2}(x) + Ax + B, \qquad (2.26)$$

$$S_{n-2}(x) = (x^2 - px - q)T_{n-4}(x) + Cx + D. \qquad (2.27)$$

Hence $P_n(w) = Aw + B$. Also

$$P_n'(x) = (2x - p)S_{n-2}(x) + (x^2 - px - q)S_{n-2}'(x) + A.$$

Since $p = w + \overline{w}$ this gives $P_n'(w) = (w - \overline{w})(Cw + D) + A$. From the Newton-Raphson formula the correction δw to the root w is

$$\delta w = -\frac{Aw + B}{(w - \overline{w})(Cw + D) + A}.$$

In general δw is small, so that the numerator of this expression is much less than the denominator and this implies that the term A in the denominator can be neglected.

Hence we can write

$$\delta w = -\frac{Aw+B}{(w-\overline{w})(Cw+D)}. \tag{2.28}$$

When we examine the division of $P_n(x)$ by a quadratic factor $x^2 - px - q$ in detail, it is found convenient to modify the above formulae in the following way. Suppose that in (2.26)

$$P_n(x) = a_0 x^n + a_1 x^{n-1} + \ldots + a_n,$$

$$S_{n-2}(x) = b_0 x^{n-2} + b_1 x^{n-3} + \ldots + b_{n-2}.$$

Then from (2.26), $b_0 = a_0$ and

$$
\begin{aligned}
b_1 &= a_1 + pb_0, \\
b_r &= a_r + pb_{r-1} + qb_{r-2}, \quad (2 \le r \le n-2), \\
A &= a_{n-1} + pb_{n-2} + qb_{n-3}, \quad B = a_n + qb_{n-2}.
\end{aligned}
\tag{2.29}
$$

If we extend (2.29) to hold for $r = n-1$ and n, thus defining b_{n-1} and b_n, we see that

$$A = b_{n-1}, \quad B = b_n - pb_{n-1}.$$

Similarly suppose that when we divide $x^2 - px - q$ into $S_{n-2}(x)$ to give (2.27) the coefficients of $T_{n-4}(x)$ are c_0, c_1, $\ldots c_{n-4}$, and we define c_{n-3}, c_{n-2} by the same rule as for c_r ($r = 2$ to $n-4$). Then we find

$$C = c_{n-3}, \quad D = c_{n-2} - pc_{n-3}.$$

On using these results in (2.28), remembering that $w + \overline{w} = p$, we obtain

$$\delta w = -\frac{b_{n-1}\overline{w} - b_n}{(w-\overline{w})(c_{n-3}\overline{w} - c_{n-2})}. \tag{2.30}$$

The computational scheme for the b_r and c_r is as follows (cf. (2.21)):

a_0	a_1	a_2	a_3	...	a_{n-2}	a_{n-1}	a_n	
	pb_0	pb_1	pb_2		pb_{n-3}	pb_{n-2}	pb_{n-1}	
		qb_0	qb_1		qb_{n-4}	qb_{n-3}	qb_{n-2}	
b_0	b_1	b_2	b_3		b_{n-2}	b_{n-1}	b_n	(2.31)
	pc_0	pc_1	pc_2		pc_{n-3}			
		qc_0	qc_1		qc_{n-4}			
c_0	c_1	c_2	c_3		c_{n-2}			

Instead of working in terms of the correction δw to the root it is convenient to work in terms of δp, δq, corrections to the quadratic factor. We have

$$(x-w-\delta w)(x-\overline{w}-\delta \overline{w}) = x^2-(p+\delta p)x-(q+\delta q),$$

so that

$$\delta p = \delta w + \delta \overline{w},$$

$$\delta q = -w\delta \overline{w}-\overline{w}\delta w-\delta w\delta \overline{w}.$$

On neglecting the second-order term in the last equation we find, on substituting from (2.30), that

$$\delta p = (b_n c_{n-3}-b_{n-1}c_{n-2})/\Delta, \qquad (2.32a)$$

$$\delta q = -(b_n c_{n-2}-b_{n-1}E)/\Delta, \qquad (2.32b)$$

where

$$\Delta = c_{n-2}^2-c_{n-3}E, \qquad (2.32c)$$

$$E = pc_{n-2}+qc_{n-3}. \qquad (2.32d)$$

These are Bairstow's formulae. They are equivalent to the following simultaneous linear equations for δp, δq:

$$c_{n-2}\delta p+c_{n-3}\delta q = -b_{n-1}, \qquad (2.33a)$$

$$E\delta p+c_{n-2}\delta q = -b_n. \qquad (2.33b)$$

The derivation given here has shown the very close relationship between Bairstow's formulae and the Newton-Raphson method.

Bairstow's method depends on locating a quadratic factor approximately before iterating to obtain the accurate factor. It should be noted that methods such as root-squaring (Graeffe's process) and the Aitken-Bernoulli process are available for calculating complex roots of polynomials even though no initial approximations are known†.

Ex. 2.6. *Find the complex roots of smallest modulus for the polynomial equation in Ex. 2.5, to four decimal places.*

As an approximation to the required quadratic factor we take the last three terms of the polynomial which give $(x^2 + 0 \cdot 1287x + 0 \cdot 1229)$. The procedure in the table (2.31), omitting the second, third, fifth, and sixth rows, which do not need to be recorded, gives

1·000 00	2·653 00	4·512 00	−2·043 00	−0·263 00	−0·251 00
1·000 00	2·524 30	4·064 22	−2·876 30	−0·392 31	0·152 99
1·000 00	2·395 60	3·633 01	−3·638 29		

From (2.32) we find

$$E = 0 \cdot 021\ 75, \qquad \Delta = 13 \cdot 158\ 14,$$

$$\delta p = -0 \cdot 066\ 23, \qquad \delta q = 0 \cdot 041\ 65.$$

On computing the new p, q and repeating the procedure we find

p	q	b_{n-1}	b_n
−0·194 93	−0·081 25	0·003 26	−0·006 83
−0·195 74	−0·083 12	−0·000 01	+0·000 03

Further iteration indicates that p, q are accurate to one unit

† See, for instance, *Modern Computing Methods*, H.M. Stationery Office, 2nd Edn. (1961).

in the fifth decimal place, and solution of the corresponding quadratic gives the complex roots $0·0979 \pm 0·2712i$, to four decimal places.

Examples II

Ex. 2.7. Find the real roots of the following equations to four significant figures

$$\text{(i)} \quad x = \cos x,$$
$$\text{(ii)} \quad x^2 - 1 = \sin x,$$
$$\text{(iii)} \quad x^x = 5.$$

Ex. 2.8. The equation $x^3 + 1·5x - 1·5 = 0$ can be written in the forms

$$\text{(i)} \quad x = 1 - \tfrac{2}{3}x^3,$$
$$\text{(ii)} \quad x = 1·5(1·5 + x^2)^{-1},$$
$$\text{(iii)} \quad x = (1·5 - 1·5x)^{\frac{1}{3}}.$$

On applying the method of § 2.2 find which of the corresponding iterative procedures are convergent. Hence determine the real root of the equation to four decimal places.

Ex. 2.9. If the root of the equation $\cot x = kx$ between 0 and $\tfrac{1}{2}\pi$ is small show that it is given approximately by $x \approx (k + \tfrac{1}{3})^{-\frac{1}{2}}$, where k is large. If the root is near $\tfrac{1}{2}\pi$ show that it is given approximately by $x \approx \tfrac{1}{2}\pi(1 + k)^{-1}$ where k is small. Use these results as first approximations to calculate the roots of the following equations to the appropriate number of significant figures, assuming that the coefficient of x in each case is correct to the last digit given:

$$\text{(i)} \quad \cot x = 111·1x,$$
$$\text{(ii)} \quad \cot x = 1·111x,$$
$$\text{(iii)} \quad \cot x = 0·011\ 11x.$$

Ex. 2.10. Use the Newton-Raphson method to obtain the following iterative formulae for $x = a^{1/n}$, $(a > 0)$:

$$f(x) = x^n - a, \qquad x_{r+1} = n^{-1}\{(n-1)x_r + ax_r^{1-n}\},$$

$$f(x) = 1 - (a/x^n), \quad x_{r+1} = n^{-1}\{(n+1)x_r - a^{-1}x_r^{n+1}\}.$$

If $x = x_r + \delta x_r$ show that in each case $\delta x_{r+1} = p_r \delta x_r^2$ for suitable p_r. Deduce that if $n > 1$ or $n < -1$ the two sequences approach x from opposite sides. Illustrate these results by calculating $\pi^{\frac{1}{2}}$, $\pi^{-\frac{1}{2}}$ by the two sequences, as accurately as possible, given $\pi = 3 \cdot 141\ 593$.

Ex. 2.11. Show that $x_{r+1} = (x_r^3 + 3ax_r)/(3x_r^2 + a)$ is a third-order procedure for the calculation of $\sqrt{a}$. Illustrate this result by calculating $\sqrt{11}$ to nine decimal places, using $x_0 = 3$. (Compare Ex. 2.2.)

Ex. 2.12. Let $y_1 = f_1(x)$, $y_2 = f_2(x)$. Show that the chord joining (x_1, y_1) to (x_2, y_2) cuts the x-axis at

$$x_3 = (x_2 y_1 - x_1 y_2)/(y_1 - y_2).$$

This is the basis of the well-known **method of false position**† for finding the roots of $f(x) = 0$: the value of $y_3 = f(x_3)$ is computed and the procedure is repeated using (x_3, y_3) instead of either (x_1, y_1) or (x_2, y_2). It is convenient to choose the two values of x at each stage so that they lie on opposite sides of the root. The method is essentially inverse linear interpolation. Use this method to solve the equations in Exs. 2.1, 2.3.

Ex. 2.13. A method due to J. H. Wegstein‡ which improves the convergence of the iterative procedure of

† E. T. Whittaker and G. Robinson, *Calculus of Observations* Blackie (1944), p. 92.

‡ Comm. Assoc. Comput. Mach. **1** (1958) No. 6, p. 9. See also G. N. Lance, *Numerical Methods for High Speed Computers*, Iliffe (1960), pp. 134-138.

§ 2.2 for solving the equation $x = F(x)$ is given by

$$X_{n+1} = \frac{x_{n+1}X_{n-1} - X_n x_n}{x_{n+1} - X_n + X_{n-1} - x_n}, \quad (n = 1, 2, \ldots),$$

where $x_{n+1} = F(X_n)$, and X_0, X_1 are arbitrary. Show that this procedure is simply a systematic version of the method of false position described in Ex. 2.12.

Ex. 2.14. Consider the following sequential calculation. If we define

$$a_0 = 1, \qquad b_0 = (1 + x^2)^{\frac{1}{2}},$$

$$a_{r+1} = \tfrac{1}{2}(a_r + b_r), \quad b_{r+1} = (b_r a_{r+1})^{\frac{1}{2}}, \quad r = 0, 1, 2, \ldots,$$

then it can be shown that, as r tends to infinity,

$$\lim a_r = \lim b_r = x/\text{arc tan } x.$$

This is not an iterative method of the type considered in this chapter since the limit depends on the starting values. In particular it is vital to avoid mistakes in the above calculation.

Ex. 2.15. Let $\pm x_1$, $\pm \bar{x}_1$, $\pm x_2$, $\pm \bar{x}_2$ denote the roots of

$$x^8 - 2(2p^2 - 0.3)x^6 + (\tfrac{1}{4}Q^4 + 6p^4 - 6p^2 + 3.73)x^4$$
$$- 2p^2(2p^4 - 3.7p^2 + 1.7)x^2 + p^4(p^2 - 1)^2 = 0.$$

Calculations on an automatic computer gave the following results ($Q = 100$):

for $p = 4$, $x_1 = 50.159 + 49.842i$, $x_2 = 0.155\,39 + 0.154\,45i$,

for $p = 10$, $x_1 = 51.017 + 49.022i$, $x_2 = 1.0139 + 0.9745i$.

Verify that for the smaller roots the formula

$$Q\left\{1 + \frac{6p^2(p^2 - 1)}{Q^4}\right\} x_2$$
$$= (1 + i)p(p^2 - 1)^{\frac{1}{2}}\left\{1 - \frac{2ip^2(p^2 - 1.85)}{(p^2 - 1)Q^2}\right\}$$

gives results correct to 1 in 15,000 for $p = 4$ and 1 in 5000 for $p = 10$. Derive a formula accurate to 1 in 10,000 for the larger roots. (The moral of this example is that even though numerical results can be obtained by an automatic computer this should not blind one to the possibility of obtaining an adequate approximate answer in analytical form.)

E

CHAPTER III

ELEMENTARY PROGRAMMING FOR AUTOMATIC COMPUTERS

§ 3.1. **Introduction.** For the purposes of this book it is unnecessary to go into detail regarding the structure of electronic digital computers; it will suffice to make some general remarks about the way in which an automatic computer works. An automatic computer has to be told precisely, and in detail, the steps which have to be performed to solve any given problem. From this point of view a calculation consists of two parts: a series of **instructions** specifying the method to be used, and a sequence of numbers leading from the data of the problem through various steps in the computation to the answer. It will be assumed that instructions and data are punched on cards which have to be fed into the machine, and that the results of a calculation are printed out by the machine on an output sheet of paper. For our purposes a digital computer can be considered to have the following components:

(a) A **memory** or store in which numbers and instructions can be stored and from which any required number can be produced at will. Each number in the memory is allocated a **memory position** or **address** which can be regarded as a pigeonhole in which the number is stored.

(b) An **input mechanism** for transferring the information on the input cards into the memory.

(c) An **output mechanism** for transferring information from the memory onto the output sheet.

(d) An **arithmetic unit** for carrying out simple basic arithmetical operations such as addition, subtraction, multiplication, division.

(e) A **control unit** which organises the calculations, i.e. arranges for the input and output of information and the execution of arithmetic operations in the correct sequence as specified by the instructions.

The set of instructions for solving a problem is called the **program**. When solving a problem the computer begins by storing the complete program in its memory *via* the input mechanism. It then proceeds to obey the instructions in an order determined by the program.

The basic instructions which a machine obeys are usually very simple. For instance it will need at least one, and perhaps several, basic orders to execute the operation " Add the two numbers contained in positions a and b in the memory and place the result in memory position c ". The reader will appreciate that to program a problem in terms of " basic machine language " would require considerable background knowledge of individual machines. It would also be very laborious. Fortunately there is an increasing tendency to produce systems by means of which a programmer can write his program in a relatively simple language resembling ordinary algebra for the formulae and ordinary terminology for the instructions. This simple language must of course be interpreted in terms of, or translated into, basic machine language before the computer can solve any given problem, but this interpretation or translation can be done by the machine itself using a " compiler ". The programmer need only prepare his program in the simple language. We shall describe a simple system of this type, devised for teaching purposes.

§ **3.2. Simple programs.** Consider the evaluation of

$$i = \frac{1}{\sqrt{\{R^2 + [2\pi fL - 1/(2\pi fC)]^2\}}}, \qquad (3.1)$$

for various sets of numbers R, L, C, f. It will be assumed that each set of R, L, C, f is punched on a separate input card. A program for this calculation can be written in the form of five **statements** as given in Program 3.1. (Instead of " statement " the words " instruction " or " order " can be used, if preferred.)

PROGRAM 3.1

LABEL	STATEMENT
9	Read R, L, C, f
	$H = 6 \cdot 2832\, fL - 1/(6 \cdot 2832\, fC)$
	$i = (R^2 + H^2)^{-\frac{1}{2}}$
	Print i, R, L, C, f
	Go to 9

The first statement makes the computer read the first card containing input data. Four numbers are on this card in the form of four sets of punched holes. The machine associates four memory positions with the symbols R, L, C, f and stores the four numbers from the input card in the corresponding memory positions. From now on, instead of saying " The number in the memory position associated with the symbol R " we shall say " The number associated with R " or, shorter still, " The number R ".

The second statement says " Perform the calculation on the right-hand side of the equation, using the numbers just associated with L, C, f. Store the result in a new memory position associated with the symbol H ". The third statement has a similar meaning: it computes and stores i. These two statements could of course be written as one single statement, but it is slightly clearer to write them separately.

The fourth statement makes the machine print the computed value of i and the values of R, L, C, f from which i has been derived.

The last statement **transfers control** to the statement numbered 9; in other words it instructs the computer " Go to the statement 9 and do what it says: then perform the statement following 9, and so on ". In Program 3.1 this means that the computer reads the next input card, which contains four new values of R, L, C, f. The computer replaces the old values in its memory by the new values and repeats the sequence of operations. The old values are lost completely when they are replaced by new values.

Instructions concerning numerical calculations, like the second and third statements in Program 3.1, are called **arithmetic statements.** The other instructions, which organise the numerical calculations, are called **control statements.**

The arithmetic statement

$$a = (x + 2 \cdot 431)/y \qquad (3.2)$$

says " Compute the number a by adding $2 \cdot 431$ to x and dividing by y ". Hence x and y must have occurred previously in any program in which this statement occurs, since the machine must go to memory positions already allocated to the symbols x and y in order to find the numbers represented by these symbols. The precise meaning of the statement depends on whether the symbol a has occurred previously in the program. If a has occurred previously there will be a memory position already associated with a. The meaning of (3.2) is then " Obliterate the number in the memory position associated with a and replace it by the number computed from the right-hand side of the equation". If a has not occurred previously the meaning is " Allocate a memory position to the new symbol a and place in this memory position the number computed from the right-hand side of the equation ". It is clear that, although arithmetic statements resemble ordinary algebraic formulae in appearance, the " = " sign is used in a different sense. No confusion can arise from this because programs contain only statements (i.e. instructions), never algebraic formulae.

The rules governing arithmetic statements can be summarised as follows:

(i) It is essential to have only one symbol on the left-hand side of a statement. (For instance (3.2) cannot be written $ay = x + 2 \cdot 431$.) This symbol may have suffixes, e.g. f_3, f_r, a_{ij}. If the suffix r is a variable parameter, for example if $r = 1, 2, \ldots n$, the value of r must have been specified earlier in the program.

(ii) Any symbol on the right-hand side of an arithmetic statement must have occurred previously in the program. (Incidentally this is why we have written $6 \cdot 2832$ in Program 3.1 instead of 2π since the symbol π has not been defined in the program. We could of course have written $\pi = 3 \cdot 1416$ as the second statement and then the third statement could have been $H = 2\pi fL - 1/(2\pi fC)$.)

(iii) Apart from (i) and (ii) any arrangement of symbols or notation which is self-explanatory according to the ordinary rules for writing and interpreting algebraic formulae will be allowed.

We next consider an extension of Program 3.1. Suppose that for any given set of R, L, C we wish the machine to compute first the value of f for which i is a maximum, namely, from (3.1),

$$F = \frac{1}{2\pi(LC)^{\frac{1}{2}}},$$

and then evaluate i for

$$f = rh, \quad r = 1(1)n, \quad h = F/n,$$

where n is a given integer. The notation $r = 1(1)n$, which
we have already met in Ex. 1.4, means that r starts at unity
and increases by steps of unity until n is reached. A
suitable set of instructions is given in Program 3.2 which
contains only one new type of statement in addition to
those in Program 3.1.

Programs 3.2(a) and 3.2(b) compute the same quantities.
We first of all consider 3.2(a). The interpretation of the
first three statements has been covered by the discussion of
Program 3.1. The fourth statement

Do up to 3 for $r = 1(1)n$

instructs the machine " Perform all statements which
immediately follow, up to and including the statement
numbered 3, n times, the first time for $r = 1$, the second
time for $r = 2$, and so on, and the last time for $r = n$.
Then go on to the statement following statement number 3."
The first time round, the machine therefore computes and
stores f_1, H_1, i_1, the second time f_2, H_2, i_2, and so on until
finally f_n, H_n, i_n are computed and stored. When this is
done the computer will print the f_s and i_s ($s = 1$ to n) and
R, L, C. The part $r = 1(1)n$ of the " Do up to " statement
obeys rules which are similar to those governing an arithmetic statement, namely that the symbol on the left may or
may not have occurred previously in the program, but any
symbols on the right must have occurred previously in the
program. Compared with Program 3.1 the " Print " order
in Programs 3.2(a), (b) has been extended to print a subscripted variable with the range of suffixes clearly indicated.
Commas are used to separate independent variables but the
word " and " is used to separate subscripted variables with
the same range.

The numbers " 9 " and " 3 " in the " Label " column of Program 3.2(a) are simply identifying tags attached to certain statements, so that these statements can be referred

PROGRAM 3.2

(a)

LABEL	STATEMENT
9	Read R, L, C, n
	$F = 0.15915 \, (LC)^{-\frac{1}{2}}$
	$h = F/n$
	Do up to 3 for $r = 1(1) \, n$
	$f_r = rh$
	$H_r = 6.2832 \, f_r L - 1/(6.2832 \, f_r C)$
3	$i_r = (R^2 + H_r^2)^{-\frac{1}{2}}$
	Print R, L, C, n, f_s and i_s for $s = 1(1) \, n$
	Go to 9

(b)

LABEL	STATEMENT
9	Read R, L, C, n
	$F = 0.15915 \, (LC)^{-\frac{1}{2}}$
	$h = F/n$
	$f = 0$
	Do up to 3 for $r = 1(1) \, n$
	$f = f + h$
	$H = 6.2832 \, fL - 1/(6.2832 \, fC)$
3	$i_r = (R^2 + H^2)^{-\frac{1}{2}}$
	Print R, L, C, n, F, h, i_s for $s = 1(1) \, n$
	Go to 9

to in control statements such " Go to " and " Do up to " in this example. For labels we use positive integers. These need not be in increasing order of magnitude. As labels,

instead of numbers we could equally well have used Greek
or Roman letters.

In Program 3.2(a) the machine stores H_r ($r = 1$ to n) although these are used only for immediate calculations, and
are not required after the corresponding i_r have been found.
Storage space can be saved by arranging the computation
as in Program 3.2(b) where for illustrative purposes we
have decided that storage and printing of all the f_r ($r = 1$ to n)
is also unnecessary.   Consider the statement

$$f = f + h.$$

This means " Take the number in the memory position
associated with f and add h to it.   Place the result in the
memory position associated with f ".   The old number
which was in f is **overwritten**.   Any subsequent reference to
f applies to the new number which has just been stored in
the memory position associated with f.   Program 3.2(b)
should now be self-explanatory.

Suppose finally that in addition to the calculation just
considered we wish to evaluate i_r for

$$f_r = rh, \quad r = n+1, \, n+2, \, \dots \, N,$$

where N is defined by the inequalities

$$i_N < p/R \leqq i_{N-1}, \quad (p < 1, \text{ given}). \tag{3.3}$$

The maximum value of i_r is $1/R$, and i_r is monotonically
decreasing for $r > n$, so that we wish to compute i_r for
increasing r until the value of i_r falls below some prescribed
fraction of the maximum value of i.   This can be done as
in Program 3.3 where the first eight statements are the
same as in Program 3.2(b) apart from the addition of a
parameter to the " Read " statement.

The point of this example is that the number N in (3.3)
is not known beforehand.   The machine has to determine
N by computing i_s for $s = n+1, \, n+2, \, \dots$, each time comparing the current value of i_s with p/R until $i_s < p/R$.   This

procedure is controlled by an " If " statement:

$$\text{If } i_s \geq p/R \text{ go to 14}$$

which instructs the machine: " If $i_s \geq p/R$ transfer control to statement 14 as in a ' Go to ' statement. If $i_s < p/R$ perform the statement immediately following the ' If ' statement, namely ' Print . . . '." In the second half of Program 3.3 we have used s, g instead of r, f. This is not essential but it emphasises that the program consists of two distinct parts. The value of s which is printed is the value assigned to the variable s when the " Print " statement is reached, and this is the same as the number N in (3.3).

The possibility of programming Yes-No decisions by means of " If " statements is one of the distinctive features of performing calculations by means of an automatic computer. The " If " statement allows the machine to control its own calculations.

From our point of view the main difficulty in programming does not lie in the arithmetical calculations themselves but in the organisation of the sequence of calculations. It is often helpful to draw a **flow-diagram**† to clarify the logical structure of the program to be used. This is illustrated for Program 3.3 in Fig. 3.1 which should be self-explanatory. A flow-diagram consists of boxes connected by lines. The boxes are essentially of two types. A **test box** or **If-box** has one input line and two output lines. The output line which is selected depends on whether the answer to the question in the box is " yes " or " no ". Any other kind of control or arithmetic statement is placed in an **assertion box**. It is convenient to make test boxes oval and assertion boxes rectangular, as in Fig. 3.1. In contrast to the relatively limited kinds of statement used in programs, any kind of statement is allowed in flow-diagrams as long

† An excellent collection of flow-diagrams (or flow-charts) is contained in *Mathematical Methods for Digital Computers*, A. Ralston and H. S. Wilf, Wiley (1960).

as the meaning is clear. A flow-diagram tends to be descriptive but the logical interconnections are described precisely. Flow-diagrams can vary from description in broad outline to description in detail. At the one extreme the flow-diagram will consist of almost equal numbers of

PROGRAM 3.3

LABEL	STATEMENT
9	Read R, L, C, n, p
	$F = 0\cdot15915\,(LC)^{-\frac{1}{2}}$
	$h = F/n$
	$f = 0$
	Do up to 3 for $r = 1(1)\,n$
	$f = f + h$
	$H = 6\cdot2832\,fL - 1/(6\cdot2832\,fC)$
3	$i_r = 1/(R^2 + H^2)^{\frac{1}{2}}$
	$s = n$
	$g = nh$
14	$s = s + 1$
	$g = g + h$
	$H = 6\cdot2832\,gL - 1/(6\cdot2832\,gC)$
	$i_s = (R^2 + H^2)^{-\frac{1}{2}}$
	If $i_s \geqq p/R$ go to 14
	Print s, i_t for $t = 1(1)\,s, R, L, C, n, p$
	Go to 9

assertion and test boxes, with little detail in the assertion boxes. At the other extreme the programmer can convert the flow-diagram into a program directly by merely removing the lines and boxes, and inserting labels and " Go to " statements as necessary. In the flow-diagram in Fig. 3.1 the control instructions are given in detail but no arithmetic information is given.

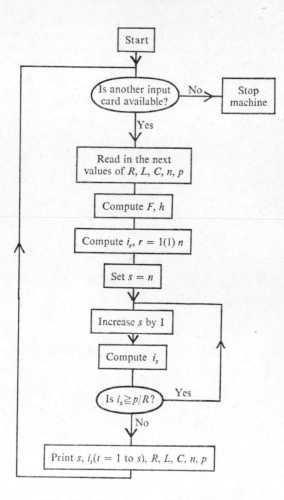

FIG. 3.1   Flow-diagram for Program 3.3

§ 3.3. Some programs involving iterative procedures.

The problems involved in programming an iterative procedure for an automatic computer can be illustrated by considering the solution of equations by means of the Newton-Raphson procedure. From § 2.3, equation (2.10), the equation $f(x) = 0$ is solved by means of the iteration

$$x_{r+1} = x_r - f(x_r)/f'(x_r),$$

where x_r is the rth approximation to the root x.

It is necessary to start by obtaining initial approximations x_0 for each of the roots which we wish to determine. It may be possible to locate the roots roughly by hand calculation and include the resulting estimates in the input data for the machine, but usually it is better to program some procedure by means of which the machine itself can make initial estimates of the roots.

The next step is to program the machine to perform the iteration. There are then two possibilities. The procedure may converge satisfactorily in which case the machine can be made to iterate until the difference between successive iterates is sufficiently small. Alternatively, the procedure may not converge or may converge extremely slowly, in which case it is necessary to alter the iteration in some way or, if desired, stop the iteration altogether.

A useful criterion for convergence is the following.†
We define $\varepsilon_r = x_{r+1} - x_r$. When an iterative procedure is converging towards a root we shall have $|\varepsilon_{r+1}| < |\varepsilon_r|$ until the ε_r become so small that they are affected by the fact that only a finite number of decimal places are used in the calculation. In simple computations we may find that $x_r = x_{r+1} = x_{r+2}$ so that $\varepsilon_r = \varepsilon_{r+1} = 0$. If the calculations are appreciably affected by round-off error, however, random error fluctuations will eventually give $|\varepsilon_{r+1}| > |\varepsilon_r|$ for some r. (Compare the discussion of random error

† This was pointed out to me by Dr D. J. Wheeler.

fluctuations in § 2.6.) In either case we can use the condition $|\varepsilon_{r+1}| \geqq |\varepsilon_r|$ as a criterion that the calculation has converged to the degree of accuracy allowed by round-off error. The level of random variations can be regarded as a **noise-level** limiting the accuracy of the calculation.

An even simpler criterion can be used if we know that the x_r vary monotonically with increasing r. Suppose for example that theoretically $x_{r+1} > x_r$ for all r. Since we are dealing with numbers specified to a finite number of decimal places we shall eventually have $x_{r+1} \leqq x_r$ due to either repetition of the iterated value, or round-off error and the noise-level of the calculation. This condition can therefore be taken as a criterion of convergence.

Some of these points are illustrated in the following examples.

Ex. 3.1. *Program* 3.4 *gives a straightforward routine for finding the square root of a positive real number a by means of the following formula (Ex. 2.2):*

$$x_{r+1} = \tfrac{1}{2}\{x_r + (a/x_r)\}.$$

If the machine is given a negative value of a by mistake this formula will give nonsensical results. In this case we make the machine stop. The value of a has been printed out, and this will indicate the source of the trouble. (This is the first time we have used the self-explanatory " Stop " order. We might have used instead an " Alarm " order to stop the machine and warn the operator that something has gone wrong with the calculation.) As an initial estimate of the root we take unity and a single iteration gives $x_0 = \tfrac{1}{2}(1+a)$. We have

$$x_r - \sqrt{a} = \tfrac{1}{2}(x_{r-1} - \sqrt{a})^2/x_{r-1} \geqq 0, \; r = 0, 1, 2, ..., \quad (3.4)$$

where for $r = 0$ we must define $x_{-1} = 1$. Hence $x_r \geqq \sqrt{a}$ and $x_r^2 \geqq a$. (This is the reason for choosing $x_0 = \tfrac{1}{2}(1+a)$. If we choose $x_0 = 1$ it would no longer be true that $x_r^2 \geqq a$

for all $r \geqq 0$.)   Equation (3.4) proves that the procedure is second-order.   From (3.4)

$$(x_r - \sqrt{a}) = \left\{ \tfrac{1}{2} \left(1 - \frac{\sqrt{a}}{x_{r-1}} \right) \right\} (x_{r-1} - \sqrt{a}).$$

Hence the procedure is convergent if

$$\tfrac{1}{2} \left| 1 - \frac{\sqrt{a}}{x_{r-1}} \right| < 1.$$

PROGRAM 3.4

LABEL	STATEMENT
	Read a
	If $a \geqq 0$ go to 12
	Print a
	Stop
12	$x = \tfrac{1}{2}(1 + a)$
2	$u = x$
	$x = \tfrac{1}{2}(x + (a/x))$
	If $x < u$ go to 2
	Print x, a
	...

Since $x_{r-1} \geqq \sqrt{a}$ for all r the procedure is always convergent. We have also

$$x_r - x_{r+1} = \tfrac{1}{2}(x_r^2 - a)/x_r \geqq 0,$$

so that successive iterates decrease until the procedure converges or reaches the noise-level of the calculation. This means that we can use the condition $x_{r+1} \geqq x_r$ as a criterion for convergence.   After the " Print x, a " order the machine goes on to the next part of the program.

One disadvantage of Program 3.4 is that if a is very different from unity then the procedure is initially somewhat slowly convergent. This is avoided in Program 3.5 where by successive multiplication or division by 16 we ensure that the iterative procedure is used only on numbers between $\frac{1}{4}$ and 4. To obtain an accuracy of say 10^{-10} it is readily verified that no more than five iterations are necessary and this fact is used in the program. The parameter r in the " Do " statement is used merely to count the number of iterations and it does not occur in any other statement. Note that the case $a = 0$ has to be considered separately.

One way in which this example is unrealistic is connected with the efficiency of the method. The square root operation will be provided as a standard routine for any machine and it will be used many millions of times per year. If we can save one millisecond in the time taken by the square root program this will save about 17 minutes of computer time every million square roots that are computed. Such economies can quickly build up into a substantial saving of computer time. Hence it is worth while devoting a considerable amount of effort to developing an efficient square-root program. The basic machine language will be used and advantage will be taken of any special features which allow time to be saved. The way in which a computation is programmed will then depend to a large extent on the way in which calculations are performed by the arithmetic unit inside the machine. Thus if all numbers inside the machine must be less than unity in magnitude and $0 < a < 1$ we cannot calculate $\frac{1}{2}(1 + a)$ by first of all forming $1 + a$, although $\frac{1}{2} + \frac{1}{2}a$ would be permissible. However, considerations of this kind lie outside the scope of this book.

Ex. 3.2. *Draw a flow-diagram for Program 3.5.*

Ex. 3.3. *Find the real roots of*

$$P_n(x) = a_0 x^n + a_1 x^{n-1} + \dots + a_n = 0.$$

PROGRAM 3.5

LABEL	STATEMENT
	Read a
	Print a
	If $a \geqq 0$ go to 12
	Stop
12	$k = 0$
	If $a > 4$ go to 3
	If $a < \frac{1}{4}$ go to 4
6	$u = \frac{1}{2}(1+a)$
	Do up to 5 for $r = 0(1)4$
5	$u = \frac{1}{2}(u+(a/u))$
	Go to 8
3	$a = a/16$
	$k = k+1$
	If $a > 4$ go to 3
	Go to 6
4	If $a > 0$ go to 7
	$x = 0$
	Go to 9
7	$a = 16a$
	$k = k-1$
	If $a < \frac{1}{4}$ go to 7
	Go to 6
8	$x = 4^k u$
	$a = 16^k a$
9	Print x, a
	...

In this example we shall use x_1, x_2, ... x_m to denote the real roots of this polynomial. (Elsewhere we have used x_r to denote the rth approximation to a root x.) Suppose that the following procedure is used. We first of all find the root of smallest absolute value x_1 and then divide $P_n(x)$ by $x - x_1$ giving a polynomial $P_{n-1}(x)$ of degree $n - 1$. We then find the next smallest root x_2 and divide $P_{n-1}(x)$ by $x - x_2$ obtaining $P_{n-2}(x)$ and so on. This sequence is repeated until we obtain x_1, x_2, ... x_m and $P_{n-m}(x)$ where this final polynomial has only complex roots. It is found that this method is very satisfactory numerically if the well-conditioned roots are found and removed first. It is for this reason that the roots are found in the order of their size, starting with the smallest, since the smaller roots tend to be better conditioned than the larger. This has already been mentioned in connection with (2.24). When finding roots by factor-removal methods it might seem desirable to try to avoid error build-up due to errors in the roots which are found first by performing final iterations on the original polynomial. However, this can be inconvenient and it is not usually necessary if the well-conditioned roots are found and removed first, since a badly conditioned root is difficult to determine accurately whether we iterate on the original polynomial or on a reduced polynomial.

The roots will be found by means of the Newton-Raphson procedure. This means that it is necessary to estimate first approximations for the roots. For the first approximation to $x_r (r > 1)$ the smallest root of $P_{n-r+1}(x)$ we shall choose x_{r-1}, the value of the smallest root of $P_{n-r+2}(x)$ which has just been found at the previous stage of the calculation. This is a reasonable procedure since if we find the smallest root at the first stage of the calculation we are likely to find the roots in increasing order of size. Also in the case where there are two roots close together, which is a troublesome case, the first of the two roots will give a close initial estimate for determination of the second.

To start the procedure we need an estimate of x_1 which we shall denote by $(x_1)_0$. This will be found in the following way. If $|a_{n-1}| \geqq |a_n|$ we set $(x_1)_0 = -a_n/a_{n-1}$; otherwise we set $(x_1)_0 = 1$. To understand why we choose $(x_1)_0$ in this way we recall that (§ 2.5 (iii))

$$-\frac{a_{n-1}}{a_n} = \frac{1}{x_1} + \frac{1}{x_2} + \ldots + \frac{1}{x_n}.$$

A large value of $|a_{n-1}/a_n|$ indicates that at least one of the x_i is small, and it is reasonable to estimate the smallest root by choosing $(x_1)_0 = -a_n/a_{n-1}$. On the other hand a small value of $|a_{n-1}/a_n|$ does not necessarily indicate that the x_i are large, since cancellation may occur. A simple example is $x^2 + 0 \cdot 0001x - 1 = 0$ where $-a_n/a_{n-1} = 10,000$ but the roots are of order unity. It would obviously be unreasonable to take $(x_1)_0 = -a_n/a_{n-1}$ in this case. If we choose $(x_1)_0 = 1$ when $|a_{n-1}| < |a_n|$ then if the smallest root is much greater than unity the Newton-Raphson procedure should still converge to it, though initially the rate of convergence may be slow; and the procedure will converge to a small root if this exists and $|a_{n-1}/a_n|$ is small merely because cancellation has occurred.

The problem of how to define $(x_1)_0$ illustrates one of the difficulties of automatic computation. The program must tell the machine exactly what to do. Ideally we should like to be certain that the value which we tell the machine to take as $(x_1)_0$ is a reasonable approximation to the smallest root. But we can always invent examples for which any specific criterion fails. The percentage of failures can be reduced by giving the machine more complicated rules for the determination of $(x_1)_0$. We have to compromise between the difficulty of programming more complicated procedures, and the desire to ensure that $(x_1)_0$ is a good approximation to the smallest root of the polynomial. The suggested procedure will not always locate all the real roots. This is partly because we are writing a general program to solve a wide class of problems. It is not surprising that we can invent examples for which the program will not work. On the whole, the more specific the problem the easier it is to write a program such that it will be virtually certain that an automatic computer will obtain the correct result.

Program 3.6 gives one method for carrying out the previously described procedure for finding the real roots of a polynomial. A flow-diagram for this program is given in Fig. 3.2. Starting at the beginning of the program, when statement 3 is reached the value $(x_1)_0$ defined above has been assigned to a variable u. After defining the values of various symbols the basic iterative procedure for finding the correction δ is performed in statements 7 to 11, using the method and notation described in some detail in § 2.5. If $|\delta/u| > 10^{-4}$ it is assumed that the process has not yet started to converge and the machine repeats the iteration. (The figure 10^{-4} is chosen arbitrarily as a figure much larger than the accuracy of the calculation which is, say, 1 in 10^{-9}, but small enough so that when $|\delta/u| < 10^{-4}$ we can be reasonably certain that the procedure is converging. Depending on circumstances it may be more convenient to work in terms of absolute instead of relative values, say $|\delta| < 10^{-4}$ indicates convergence.) If $|\delta/u| < 10^{-4}$ on the first iteration the program defines a variable $\varepsilon = \delta$ and then repeats the iteration. In general the program sets ε equal to the old value of δ before starting an iteration to find a new δ. If the iteration is converging normally we have $|\delta| < |\varepsilon|$. We assume that when, after a period of normal convergence, $|\delta| \geqq |\varepsilon|$ the process has converged and the root has been determined to the maximum possible accuracy for the method used. The current values of u and δ are printed out, where δ is the next correction to u and gives some idea of the " noise-level " of the calculation. (This idea could be extended by asking the machine to perform say four iterations beyond the point where $|\delta| \geqq |\varepsilon|$, and record the maximum and minimum values

PROGRAM 3.6

LABEL	STATEMENT
	Read a_i for $i = 0(1)\ n$
	Print a_i for $i = 0(1)\ n$
	$u = 1$
	If $|a_{n-1}| < |a_n|$ go to 3
	$u = -a_n/a_{n-1}$
3	$b_0 = a_0$
	$c_0 = a_0$
	$j = 1$
5	$r = 0$
	go to 7
6	$\varepsilon = \delta$
	$u = u + \delta$
7	Do up to 10 for $m = 1(1)\ n-j+1$
	$b_m = a_m + b_{m-1}u$
10	$c_m = b_m + c_{m-1}u$
11	$\delta = -b_{n-j+1}/c_{n-j}$
	If $|\delta/u| < 10^{-4}$ go to 12
	$r = r+1$
	If $r < 20$ go to 6
	Print $u,\ \delta,\ a_i$ for $i = 0(1)\ n-j+1$
20	Stop
12	If $r = 0$ go to 6
	If $|\delta| < |\varepsilon|$ go to 6
	Print $u,\ \delta$
	If $j = n$ go to 20
	$j = j+1$
	Do up to 15 for $m = 1(1)\ n-j+1$
15	$a_m = b_m$
	Go to 5

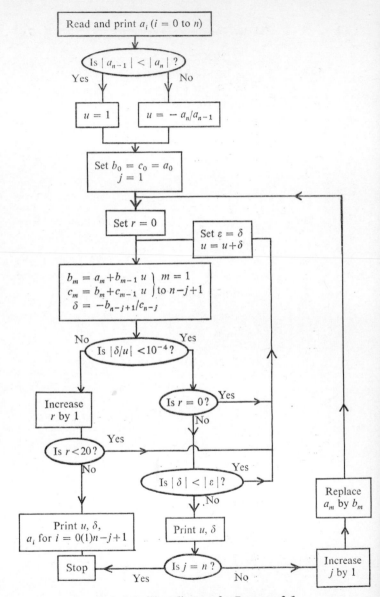

FIG. 3.2 Flow-diagram for Program 3.6

of u. Note that it is a better check on the accuracy of the calculation to print out δ than to print out the residuals which may be small even though the roots are inaccurate, as shown in § 2.6.) Once the process has converged the program tests to see if $j = n$ which indicates that the polynomial has real roots, all of which have been found. If this is the case the calculation is stopped. Otherwise the new polynomial $P_{n-j}(x)$ is set in place of $P_{n-j+1}(x)$ and the iteration is repeated. The variable u is already set up as the root of $P_{n-j+1}(x)$ which has just been found, and this is the appropriate first approximation to the smallest root of $P_{n-j}(x)$.

§ 3.4. **General comments.** We shall illustrate briefly some differences between automatic and hand computing by considering the problem of finding the real roots of a polynomial, assuming that the program of Ex. 3.3 is used for the automatic computer and a similar method is used for the computation by hand.

(i) In hand computing a convenient method for locating the roots is to evaluate $f(\infty)$, $f(0)$, $f(-\infty)$ and then $f(x)$ for suitable intermediate x. We should probably draw a rough graph of $y = f(x)$. Although it is not impossible to program this type of procedure we have preferred a simpler method for the automatic computer program.

(ii) In hand computing, when calculating the smallest root of each of the polynomials $P_{n-j}(x)$ we would usually try to obtain an accurate first approximation for this root rather than merely taking the root of $P_{n-j+1}(x)$ found at the previous stage of the calculation.

(iii) In hand computing we can control the number of decimal places used in the calculation. If the final answer is required to a large number of decimal places we would use a comparatively small number of decimal places in the early stages but increase the accuracy as the procedure converges. There is no point in doing this with an automatic computer.

(iv) In hand computing we would decide the number of decimal places accuracy required in the final result and adjust the calculation accordingly. In automatic computing it is simpler to work to the full accuracy available in the machine and determine the " noise-level " for each root.

(v) In hand computing we would check at the end of the calculation that we have located all the real roots. We have not incorporated any such check in our program. When using a computer it might be simpler to merely calculate all the roots, both real and complex, and then we should be sure that all the real roots have been determined.

(vi) In hand computing a convenient check is to divide the final polynomial with complex roots into the original polynomial, which should give zero remainder, though there will in fact be a small remainder from inaccuracies due to rounding-off error. We can then check that the sum and product of the known roots agree with the appropriate coefficients of the dividend. In automatic computing it is probably unnecessary to apply this check.

The following are some general comments.

On the whole, in programming for an automatic computer we prefer a numerical method which involves a simple repetitive procedure, even though this is repeated a large number of times, to a method involving a complicated procedure which is repeated only a few times. The reverse is often true in hand computing.

In hand computation the total number of operations involved is usually comparatively small and the effect of round-off errors can usually be made negligible merely by keeping one or two extra decimal places. In automatic computing the calculations tend to be large in scale and the number of arithmetical operations may be enormous. It may be much more difficult to estimate the effects of errors of various kinds and it may be important to use methods which minimise certain kinds of error.

The possibility of an automatic computer making arithmetical mistakes can be ignored when using systems of the type described in this chapter. In this respect computation by an automatic machine is very different from hand computation. On the other hand errors such as loss of significant figures caused by subtracting two large nearly equal numbers to give a small one may be much more serious than in hand computation since they may easily pass undetected. It is most important to bear in mind that we have no information about what goes on in an automatic computer between the input figures and the figures which are printed out. Whereas in hand computation we often recognise loss of accuracy or misleading results due to unsuitable methods, while doing the calculation, an automatic computer will not do this for us unless we realise beforehand that this may occur and allow for it in the program.

Other aspects of the suitability of methods for automatic computers will be mentioned in connection with the various topics dealt with later in this book.

The main objects of describing the simplified programming scheme in this chapter are threefold.

(a) To give the student some idea of how a program is organised for an automatic computer. The machine must be told in detail what to do, but it can control its own calculations to a limited extent.

(b) To give the student a programming system by means of which he can write his own programs for the standard methods used in numerical analysis. We have already illustrated this in connection with the Newton-Raphson procedure and further examples will occur throughout this book.

(c) To give the student some understanding of the differences between hand computing and machine computing, and of the criteria which govern whether a method is suitable for automatic computing.

However, the reader should not be misled by the simplicity of the programming system and programs in this book. One of the major preoccupations of anyone using an automatic computer is the efficiency of the procedure used, since computer time is expensive. In practice full advantage is taken of special features of a computer and its programming system in order to devise the easiest and cheapest method for doing a particular problem on a particular machine. These factors often over-ride purely mathematical considerations. They lie outside the scope of this book.

Examples III

Ex. 3.4. It is required to find a real root of an equation $f(x) = 0$ by means of the following procedure. Two numbers a and b are given such that $f(a) < 0, f(b) > 0$. We define a sequence x_r, y_r by the equations

$$x_0 = a, \ y_0 = b$$

$$\begin{cases} x_{r+1} = \tfrac{1}{2}(x_r + y_r), & y_{r+1} = y_r, & \text{if} \quad f\{\tfrac{1}{2}(x_r + y_r)\} \leqq 0, \\ x_{r+1} = x_r, & y_{r+1} = \tfrac{1}{2}(x_r + y_r), & \text{if} \quad f\{\tfrac{1}{2}(x_r + y_r)\} > 0. \end{cases}$$

(i) Write a program to determine a root to within 10^{-m}, where m is an integer specified in the input data, and it is assumed that the number of significant figures used in the machine will allow determination of the root to the required degree of accuracy.

(ii) Write a program to determine the root to the maximum number of significant digits allowed by the accuracy of the evaluation of $f(x)$, assuming that this is limited by round-off error.

(Assume that " Read $f(x)$ " means that a set of instructions is given to the machine for evaluating $f(x)$. Whenever $f(y)$ for instance, occurs on the right of an arithmetic statement the machine will evaluate $f(x)$ for $x = y$ and use the resulting number in the appropriate place in the arithmetic statement.)

Ex. 3.5. Write a program for finding arc tan x by the sequential procedure given in Ex. 2.14.

Ex. 3.6. Write a program (or a flow-diagram) for computing $\sin x$ and $\cos x$ for any value of x, $-\infty < x < \infty$, given that for $0 < u \leq \pi/6$

$$\sin u = \frac{a_1 u}{u^2 + a_2 + a_3(u^2 + a_4)^{-1}},$$

$$\cos u = \frac{b_1}{u^2 + b_2 + b_3(u^2 + b_4)^{-1}},$$

where the $a_i(i = 1 \text{ to } 4)$, $b_i(i = 1 \text{ to } 4)$ are given constants. For $\pi/6 < 2v < \pi/3$ use the relations

$$\cos 2v = 2 \cos^2 v - 1, \quad \sin 2v = \cos (\tfrac{1}{2}\pi - 2v).$$

(The formulae for sin, cos, are discussed in A. Ralston and H. S. Wilf, *Mathematical Methods for Digital Computers*, Wiley (1960), p. 23.)

Ex. 3.7. Write a program for evaluating the n smallest positive roots of the equation $\cot x = kx$ by an iterative procedure for $k = a(b)c$ (cf. Ex. 2.9). Outline briefly some of the principal differences between the way in which this calculation could be performed on an automatic computer, and the way in which it could be performed by desk calculator. (In addition to the points in § 3.4, for hand computation we should use mathematical tables for $\cot x$ whereas in a computer functions need to be calculated. This may influence the choice of method. In hand computing we should check by differences as in § 7.3 below.)

CHAPTER IV

SIMULTANEOUS LINEAR ALGEBRAIC EQUATIONS

§ 4.1. Introduction. Very many problems in applied mathematics can be reduced to the solution of a set of simultaneous linear algebraic equations. It is therefore of great importance to have efficient methods for the numerical solution of such systems.

If we consider the equations

$$a_{11}x_1 + a_{12}x_2 + \quad \ldots \quad + a_{1n}x_n = b_1,$$
$$\cdot \qquad \cdot \qquad \cdot \qquad \cdot \qquad (4.1)$$
$$a_{n1}x_1 + a_{n2}x_2 + \quad \ldots \quad + a_{nn}x_n = b_n,$$

the solution can be written, by Cramer's rule,†

$$x_j = \Delta_j/\Delta, \quad (j = 1 \text{ to } n), \qquad (4.2)$$

where

$$\Delta = \begin{vmatrix} a_{11} & \ldots & a_{1n} \\ & \cdot \quad \cdot \quad \cdot & \\ a_{n1} & \ldots & a_{nn} \end{vmatrix} \neq 0,$$

and Δ_j is Δ with the jth column replaced by the column of bs. This solution is useful for certain kinds of problem but it is seldom used in numerical work when the coefficients are pure numbers since much more efficient methods are available for this case. As a general rule the direct evaluation of determinants is laborious and inefficient and should be avoided wherever possible in numerical work.

† See A. C. Aitken, *Determinants and Matrices*, Oliver and Boyd (1962), p. 55.

The above solution is of theoretical interest. It breaks down when Δ, the determinant of the coefficients, is zero. In this case we may have either a multiplicity of solutions (when the Δ_j are also zero) or inconsistent equations with no solution (where at least one of the Δ_j is non-zero, so that if we imagine a limiting procedure in which Δ tends to zero, the formula (4.2) gives apparently infinite x_j). We need not go into detail since it will be assumed, when solving simultaneous linear equations, that the determinant of the coefficients is non-zero. It can be anticipated, however, that difficulties will arise if Δ is nearly equal to zero (see § 4.4 below). If the b_i in (4.1) are zero then the Δ_j in (4.2) are zero, and non-zero x_j exist only if $\Delta = 0$. This case is of importance in Chapter VI.

It is convenient to distinguish between **direct** and **iterative** methods of solution of linear equations. The amount of computation involved in direct methods can be specified in advance whereas an iterative computation is repeated until the error is less than the required amount. Direct methods are discussed in this chapter and the next. Iterative methods are discussed in § 6.4.

When dealing with numerical examples we shall omit the x_j and the addition and equality signs in (4.1) and write merely an array of numbers:

$$a_{11} \quad a_{12} \quad \cdots \quad a_{1n} \quad b_1$$
$$\cdot \qquad \cdot \qquad \cdot \qquad \cdot$$
$$a_{n1} \quad a_{n2} \quad \cdots \quad a_{nn} \quad b_n$$

When working to a fixed number of decimal places it is usually essential to arrange that the largest element in each row and column of this array is of order unity. This can be done by multiplying the original equations by constants and introducing suitable (preferably simple) multiples of the unknowns. We return to this point later (§ 4.3). If the original coefficients are such that $a_{ij} = a_{ji}$ (i.e. if the a_{ij} are symmetrical about the principal diagonal $a_{11}, a_{22}, \ldots a_{nn}$) the scaling should be arranged to preserve the symmetry.

Ex. 4.1. *Scale the equations*

$$
\begin{aligned}
80X_1 + \quad\;\; 5X_2 - \quad\;\;\; 0{\cdot}2X_3 &= \quad\; 2{\cdot}8, \\
5X_1 - \quad\; 0{\cdot}2X_2 + \;\; 0{\cdot}0125X_3 &= -0{\cdot}0875, \\
-0{\cdot}2X_1 + 0{\cdot}0125X_2 + \; 0{\cdot}00625X_3 &= -0{\cdot}025.
\end{aligned}
$$

The scaling factors that should be used are more or less arbitrary. If, for example, we introduce

$$x_1 = 40X_1, \quad x_2 = 2X_2, \quad x_3 = 0{\cdot}5X_3,$$

and multiply the equations by 1, 20, 80 respectively, we obtain

$$
\begin{aligned}
2x_1 + 2{\cdot}5x_2 - 0{\cdot}4x_3 &= 2{\cdot}8, \\
2{\cdot}5x_1 - \quad 2x_2 + 0{\cdot}5x_3 &= -1{\cdot}75, \qquad (4.3) \\
-0{\cdot}4x_1 + 0{\cdot}5x_2 + \quad\;\; x_3 &= -2.
\end{aligned}
$$

§ 4.2. The method of successive elimination. The method of successive elimination is well-known in elementary algebra. Thus to solve (4.3) we can subtract $1{\cdot}25$ times the first equation from the second, and add $0{\cdot}2$ times the first equation to the third. This gives two equations in x_2, x_3. Similarly x_2 can be eliminated from these two equations to give x_3. Then back-substitution in previous equations yields x_2, x_1 in succession.

The object of this section is to describe a tabular procedure, with frequent checks, for the practical application of this method when the coefficients are given decimal numbers. The calculation and the checks can be arranged in the tabular form given below. Although this is written out only for a set of four equations in four unknowns, the procedure in the general case should be clear. The square brackets will be explained later in Ex. 5.4. The numbers in round brackets are used for checks.

	a_{11}	a_{12}	a_{13}	a_{14}	b_1	(s_1)	(4.4)
l_{21}	a_{21}	a_{22}	a_{23}	a_{24}	b_2	(s_2)	
l_{31}	a_{31}	a_{32}	a_{33}	a_{34}	b_3	(s_3)	
l_{41}	a_{41}	a_{42}	a_{43}	a_{44}	b_4	(s_4)	
	(S_1)	(S_2)	(S_3)	(S_4)	(S_5)	$(S = s)$	
		b_{22}	b_{23}	b_{24}	c_2	$(t_2 \approx T_2)$	(4.5)
l_{32}		$[b_{32}$	b_{33}	b_{34}	c_3	$(t_3 \approx T_3)]$	(4.6)
l_{42}		$[b_{42}$	b_{43}	b_{44}	c_4	$(t_4 \approx T_4)]$	(4.7)
			c_{33}	c_{34}	d_3	$(u_3 \approx U_3)$	(4.8)
l_{43}			$[c_{43}$	c_{44}	d_4	$(u_4 \approx U_4)]$	(4.9)
				d_{44}	e_4	$(v_4 \approx V_4)$	(4.10)

Roots:

$$x_1 \quad x_2 \quad x_3 \quad x_4 \quad (S_5' \approx S_5)$$

The first step is to form check sums which will be used later:

$$s_i = a_{i1} + a_{i2} + a_{i3} + a_{i4} + b_i, \quad (i = 1 \text{ to } 4),$$
$$S_j = a_{1j} + a_{2j} + a_{3j} + a_{4j}, \quad\quad (j = 1 \text{ to } 4),$$
$$S_5 = b_1 + b_2 + b_3 + b_4,$$
$$s = s_1 + s_2 + s_3 + s_4,$$
$$S = S_1 + S_2 + S_3 + S_4 + S_5.$$

We should find $s = S$ *exactly* since no round-off errors are involved, and this is the first check on the numerical work. We then calculate

$$l_{21} = a_{21}/a_{11}, \quad l_{31} = a_{31}/a_{11}, \quad l_{41} = a_{41}/a_{11}.$$

The 4×4 set of equations is reduced to a 3×3 set by eliminating the first unknown:

$$b_{ij} = a_{ij} - l_{i1}a_{1j}, \quad (i, j = 2, 3, 4), \tag{4.11}$$

$$c_i = b_i - l_{i1}b_1,$$

$$t_i = s_i - l_{i1}s_1. \tag{4.12}$$

Note that the steps involved in applying these three formulae are of exactly the same kind, so that the procedure is easily reduced to a routine. This holds also for the similar eliminations which follow later. The b_{ij}, c_i, t_i are calculated line by line and at the end of each line we perform a check by calculating

$$T_i = b_{i2} + b_{i3} + b_{i4} + c_i, \quad (i = 2, 3, 4), \tag{4.13}$$

which should agree with the t_i to within a unit or two in the last significant figure, any difference being due to rounding errors.

In the same way we calculate

$$l_{32} = b_{32}/b_{22}, \quad l_{42} = b_{42}/b_{22}.$$

The 3×3 set of equations is reduced to a 2×2 set by forming

$$c_{ij} = b_{ij} - l_{i2}b_{2j}, \quad (i, j = 3, 4), \tag{4.14}$$

with similar equations for d_i, u_i, and a check

$$U_i = c_{i3} + c_{i4} + d_i, \quad (i = 3, 4),$$

which should agree approximately with u_i.

The 2×2 set of equations is reduced to a single equation by

$$l_{43} = c_{43}/c_{33}, \tag{4.15}$$

$$d_{44} = c_{44} - l_{43}c_{34},$$

with similar equations for e_4, v_4. Also $V_4 = d_{44} + e_4 \approx v_4$.

At this stage we have reduced the original equations to

the system (4.4), (4.5), (4.8), (4.10):

$$a_{11}x_1 + a_{12}x_2 + a_{13}x_3 + a_{14}x_4 = b_1$$
$$b_{22}x_2 + b_{23}x_3 + b_{24}x_4 = c_2 \qquad (4.16)$$
$$c_{33}x_3 + c_{34}x_4 = d_3$$
$$d_{44}x_4 = e_4.$$

The unknowns can now be found by back-substitution. We have

$$x_4 = e_4/d_{44},$$
$$x_3 = (d_3 - c_{34}x_4)/c_{33}, \text{ etc.}$$

A check on the final answer is provided by the equation

$$S_5' = S_1x_1 + S_2x_2 + S_3x_3 + S_4x_4.$$

S_5' should agree with the previously computed S_5 except possibly for a small difference due to rounding-off errors. However, agreement between S_5 and S_5' to a given number of decimal places does not necessarily indicate that the x_i are accurate to this number of places (see § 4.4).

A group of m sets of equations with the same a_{ij} but m different right-hand sides $b_{ik}(k = 1$ to $m)$ can be solved by including m columns b_{ik} instead of a single column b_i. Only one check column is needed, obtained by adding all the elements in the corresponding rows.

Ex. 4.2. *A numerical example is worked on the following page. An extra figure is carried in the intermediate calculation, but the roots are rounded to four decimal places.*

The positions of numbers correspond exactly with those given earlier except for the occurrence of only a single number in the right-hand check columns. Consider, for example, t_3 and T_3 in (4.6). In the numerical calculation, instead of writing down the two numbers separately, we first of all write down t_3 using formula (4.12) which gives

G

	x_1	x_2	x_3	x_4	b_i	Checks
	0·5400	0·5233	0·4358	0·3622	1·3015	(3·1628)
	0·5233	0·7872	0·3622	0·5257	0·2415	(2·4399)
	0·4358	0·3622	0·3881	0·2973	1·2706	(2·7540)
	0·3622	0·5257	0·2973	0·4377	0·1826	(1·8055)
	(1·8613)	(2·1984)	(1·4834)	(1·6229)	(2·9962)	(10·1622)
0·969 07		0·280 09	−0·060 12	0·174 70	−1·019 74	(−0·625 07)
0·807 04		−0·060 12	0·036 39	0·004 99	0·220 24	(0·201 4950)
0·670 74		0·174 70	−0·004 99	0·194 76	−0·690 37	(−0·315 92)
−0·214 65			0·023 49	0·042 49	0·001 35	(0·067 33)
0·623 73			0·042 49	0·085 79	−0·054 33	(0·073 954)
1·808 85				0·008 93	−0·056 77	(0·047 854)
Roots:	−5·3708	2·8050	11·5568	−6·3572	(2·9961)	

0·201 49. We then calculate T_3 using formula (4.13) and this gives 0·201 50. The difference between t_3 and T_3 is permissible. For checking the next stage of the calculation it is necessary to use the exact row sum T_3, not t_3 (why not?), so we amend the recorded value of t_3 by crossing out the last two digits, and replacing them by 50.

In this example, since the square array of coefficients a_{ij} is symmetrical about the diagonal line containing a_{11}, a_{22}, a_{33}, a_{44}, each of the square arrays derived from these coefficients is symmetrical, apart from small differences due to rounding-off errors. This can be used as a check, or only half the non-diagonal terms need be computed.

§ 4.3. Choice of pivots and scaling.

In our description of the method of successive elimination in the last section the element in the top left-hand corner of each array plays a very special part. It is called the **pivot**. The l_{ij} are obtained by dividing each of the other elements in the same column as the pivot by the pivot. It is obvious that in any given array any non-zero element can be used as the pivot. Suppose that in the a_{ij} array we choose a_{rs} as the pivot. The rth row, which contains the pivot, is set aside. We calculate, from the elements in the sth column

$$l_{is} = a_{is}/a_{rs}, \quad (i = 1 \text{ to } 4, \text{ omitting } i = r).$$

Then

$$b_{ij} = a_{ij} - l_{is}a_{rj},$$

where $i = 1$ to 4, $j = 1$ to 4 omitting $i = r$, $j = s$, i.e. the row and column containing the pivot. The routine is exactly as before.

In the elimination procedure of § 4.2, equations (4.1) with $n = 4$ were reduced to the form (4.16). It is easy to see that the determinant of coefficients has not been altered since one determinant is obtained from the other by adding multiples of certain rows to other rows:

$$\Delta = \begin{vmatrix} a_{11} & a_{12} & a_{13} & a_{14} \\ a_{21} & a_{22} & a_{23} & a_{24} \\ a_{31} & a_{32} & a_{33} & a_{34} \\ a_{41} & a_{42} & a_{43} & a_{44} \end{vmatrix} = \begin{vmatrix} a_{11} & a_{12} & a_{13} & a_{14} \\ 0 & b_{22} & b_{23} & b_{24} \\ 0 & 0 & c_{33} & c_{34} \\ 0 & 0 & 0 & d_{44} \end{vmatrix}$$

$$= a_{11}b_{22}c_{33}d_{44}. \tag{4.17}$$

This is an important result, that the determinant of the coefficients of the original equations is given by the product of the pivots. It can be proved in the same way that this result holds however the pivots are chosen, apart possibly from the sign of the determinant.

It is sometimes stated without qualification that the largest element in an array should always be chosen as the pivot but the importance of this can be over-rated. Before discussing this we consider an example.

Ex. 4.3. *Solve the equations in Ex. 4.2 by the method of successive elimination, using the largest element in each array as the pivot.*

If we assume that the coefficients of the equations in Exs. 4.2, 4.3 are exact and solve the equations using a large number of decimal places in the intermediate calculations we find that the exact roots are

$$x_1 = -5 \cdot 3868, \ x_2 = 2 \cdot 8137, \ x_3 = 11 \cdot 5729, \ x_4 = -6 \cdot 3653, \tag{4.18}$$

rounded to four decimals. The differences between this exact solution and the results in Exs. 4.2, 4.3 are given in Table 4.1 which shows that, in this particular example, the results obtained by taking the largest pivot at each stage are less accurate than the results obtained by choosing the top left-hand pivot. The reason for this is the smallness of the final pivot in Ex. 4.3, namely $0 \cdot 002 \ 51$, which is considerably smaller

	x_1	x_2	x_3	x_4	b_i
0.664 76	0·5400	0·5233	0·4358	0·3622	1·3015
	0·5233	0·7872	0·3622	0·5257	0·2415
0.460 11	0·4358	0·3622	0·3881	0·2973	1·2706
0.667 81	0·3622	0·5257	0·2973	0·4377	0·1826
0.880 65	0·192 13		0·195 02	0·012 74	1·140 96
0.250 26	0·195 02		0·221 45	0·055 42	1·159 48
	0·012 74		0·055 42	0·086 63	0·021 32
−0.495 74	0·020 39			−0·036 07	0·119 86
	−0·036 07			0·072 76	−0·268 85
0.002 51	0·002 51				−0·013 42
Roots:	−5·3466	2·7924	11·5324	−6·3455	

than 0·008 93, the smallest pivot in Ex. 4.2. The size of the smallest pivot in Ex. 4.3 limits the accuracy of the roots to at most 1 in 500, in general. The reason for the very small final pivot in Ex. 4.3 is clear from (4.17) which states that the product of the pivots must be a constant. If we insist on choosing as pivot the largest number available at each stage this tends to lead to smaller pivots than might otherwise be obtained. The logical conclusion of this argument might seem to be that the pivots should be chosen so that they are all nearly equal to each other, and therefore each

TABLE 4.1

Comparison of solutions obtained by the method of successive elimination

$$\delta_i = (x_i)_{\text{true}} - (x_i)_{\text{calc}}.$$

Top left pivots (Ex. 4.2)	−0·0160	0·0087	0·0161	−0·0081
Largest pivots (Ex. 4.3)	−0·0402	0·0213	0·0405	−0·0198
Top left pivots, after scaling	−0·0098	0·0055	0·0099	−0·0052
Largest pivots, after scaling	0·0148	−0·0077	−0·0149	0·0071

pivot should be roughly equal to the nth root of the determinant. Apart from the fact that this is impractical since the determinant is not known at the beginning of the analysis it is not true that increasing the size of the smallest pivot automatically increases the accuracy. It will be shown in the next section that a certain inherent inaccuracy is present in the roots of a set of simultaneous linear equations if these are found by any procedure involving rounding-off errors. As long as the pivots are large enough so that round-off in the smallest pivot does not imply a relative error greater than the inherent error in the calculation, it would seem that little additional accuracy can be obtained by choosing the pivots in any special way. The essential point is to avoid very small pivots rather than to arrange that the smallest pivot is as large as possible. On the whole the size of the pivots would seem to be of second-order importance.

In § 4.5 below, when programming the method of successive elimination for automatic computers, we shall pivot on the largest element in the left-hand column of numbers in the array obtained after each elimination. This avoids unnecessarily small pivots, and the multipliers are all less than unity which may be convenient for some computers.

The object of illustrating that the choice of pivots in Ex. 4.2 gives more accurate results than the choice in Ex. 4.3 is not of course to imply that the choice of the top left-hand number as pivot is to be preferred to the choice of the largest pivot at each stage. Many of the equations which occur in practice are such that, when calculating by hand, they are suitable for solution by choosing the top left-hand number as pivot even though this is not the largest possible pivot. On the other hand if the top left-hand number is appreciably smaller than the other numbers in an array then it should certainly not be chosen as pivot.

Suppose next that we rescale the equations of Exs. 4.2, 4.3 by multiplying the third equation by two and the fourth equation by four and introduce new unknowns

$$x_1' = x_1, \quad x_2' = x_2, \quad x_3' = \tfrac{1}{2}x_3, \quad x_4' = \tfrac{1}{4}x_4.$$

It will be found that if the pivots are chosen as the top left-hand numbers in each array as in Ex. 4.2 the pivots are

$$0{\cdot}5400, \quad 0{\cdot}280\,09, \quad 0{\cdot}093\,96, \quad 0{\cdot}142\,90.$$

If the pivots are chosen to be the largest numbers at each stage as in Ex. 4.3 then the pivots are

$$7{\cdot}0032, \quad 0{\cdot}744\,65, \quad 0{\cdot}155\,67, \quad 0{\cdot}002\,49.$$

The differences between the exact results and the results

given by the two methods are given in Table 4.1. It is seen that although scaling has improved the results slightly the improvement is not striking. The smallest pivot when using the top left-hand pivots is now comparatively large, but the smallest pivot obtained by taking the largest pivot at each stage is almost exactly the same as in Ex. 4.3 before rescaling.

The point about rescaling is exactly the same as the point previously made about the choice of pivot. Rescaling can be advantageous in avoiding very small pivots rather than arranging that the smallest pivot should be as large as possible. Once the smallest pivot is above a certain minimum value there is little point in further rescaling.

In practice if it turns out that the smallest pivot is undesirably small it is usually preferable to improve the solution by the method described in the next section (Ex. 4.4) rather than repeat the solution with a different choice of pivots, rescaled equations, or more decimal places.

§ 4.4. **Inherent error and ill-conditioned equations.** This section is concerned with a characteristic difficulty which occurs when solving linear equations. We first consider a concrete example:

$$1 \cdot 985 x_1 - 1 \cdot 358 x_2 = 2 \cdot 212, \qquad (4.19)$$
$$0 \cdot 953 x_1 - 0 \cdot 652 x_2 = 1 \cdot 062.$$

Elimination of x_1 gives

$$(1 \cdot 985 \times 0 \cdot 652 - 0 \cdot 953 \times 1 \cdot 358) x_2$$
$$= - (1 \cdot 985 \times 1 \cdot 062 - 0 \cdot 953 \times 2 \cdot 212). \qquad (4 \cdot 20)$$

On working to six decimal places we find

$$0 \cdot 000 \ 046 x_2 = -0 \cdot 000 \ 034, \quad x_2 = -0 \cdot 739....$$

Similarly $x_1 = 0 \cdot 609....$ In quoting the answers to three decimal places we have in fact assumed that the coefficients in (4.19) are correct to seven decimal places and that we have worked to seven decimal places so that $x_2 = -340/460$, $x_1 = 280/460$. If after evaluating the quantities in brackets in (4.20) we had to round off to five decimal places we have $x_2 = -0.000\,03/0.000\,05 = -0.6...$, and the answer is not even correct to one decimal place. Round-off imposes a fundamental limitation on the accuracy with which the roots can be obtained.

If instead of (4.19) we solve

$$1.985x_1 - 1.358x_2 = 2.212,$$
$$0.953x_1 - 0.652x_2 = 1.061,$$

we find $x_1 = 30.01...$, $x_2 = 42.41...$. An alteration of one coefficient of (4.19) by one in a thousand (1.062 changed to 1.061) has altered the roots by factors of about fifty to one (0.61 to 30, and -0.74 to 42).

The reason for the behaviour of the above equation is clear. The second equation is nearly a multiple of the first so that we can write the equations algebraically as

$$ax_1 + bx_2 = c,$$
$$(ka + \alpha)x_1 + (kb + \beta)x_2 = kc + \gamma,$$

where k is a suitable constant and α, β, γ are small. The roots of these equations are

$$x_1 = \frac{c\beta - b\gamma}{a\beta - b\alpha}, \quad x_2 = -\frac{c\alpha - a\gamma}{a\beta - b\alpha}.$$

The small numbers α, β, γ have a dominant effect on the result. In computing determinants, large numbers have cancelled by subtraction to give small final results. The determinant of coefficients is small relative to the individual terms in the expansion of the determinant. (Notice that it is meaningless to say that the determinant is small—it has to be small relative to some other quantity.)

If X_i are approximate roots of the set of linear equations (4.1) we define the **residuals** r_i as

$$r_i = \sum_{j=1}^{n} a_{ij}X_j - b_i. \qquad (4.21)$$

For equations (4.19), if we take $X_1 = 0\cdot638$, $X_2 = -0\cdot696$ we find

$$r_1 = -0\cdot0004, \quad r_2 = -0\cdot0002.$$

Roots which differ from the true roots by 1 in 20 produce residuals which are less than the round-off error of the coefficients. This illustrates the important point that *smallness of the residuals does not necessarily mean that the corresponding estimates of the roots are accurate.*

Equations like (4.19) are said to be **ill-conditioned**. The opposite of ill-conditioned is **well-conditioned**. We talk of the " condition " or " conditioning " of a set of equations.

As already illustrated, characteristic signs of ill-conditioning are:

(a) To determine the roots to a specified number of decimal places when round-off error is present it is necessary to work to a much larger number of decimal places in the intermediate calculations.

(b) Small alterations in the coefficients produce large variations in the roots.

(c) The determinant of the coefficients is small in the sense described above.

(d) Estimates of the roots which differ appreciably from the true roots produce very small residuals.

Two other indications of ill-conditioning depend on ideas which will be introduced later. In terms of the inverse matrix defined in § 5.3, equations are ill-conditioned if the elements of the inverse matrix are large in the sense described at the end of Ex. 5.6. In terms of the concept of an eigen-value defined in Chapter VI, equations are ill-conditioned if the ratio of the largest to smallest eigenvalue of the matrix of coefficients is large.

The equations in Ex. 4.2 are slightly ill-conditioned (see also Ex. 5.6).

If the diagonal elements a_{11}, a_{22}, ... a_{nn} are much greater than the non-diagonal elements a_{ij} $(i \neq j)$ then the equations are well-conditioned. If all a_{ij} $(i \neq j)$ are zero then the equations are perfectly conditioned. If the coefficients vary in size it is usually convenient to arrange, by interchange of equations and/or scaling, that the largest coefficients lie in or near the diagonal positions $a_{11}, a_{22}, ... a_{nn}$.

It is useful to distinguish between two different aspects of accuracy when solving linear equations.

(i) If the coefficients of the equations are assumed to be exact but a fixed number of decimal places are carried during the solution, how many decimal places are accurate in the answer?

(ii) If the coefficients of the equation are inexact (for example because they are obtained by rounding off more accurate numbers) to how many places are we justified in quoting the final answer?

It is easy to answer both of these questions in any specific case, provided that the detailed solution of the original equations is available and we are prepared to do a little extra work. Suppose that in case (i) the roots obtained by working to a fixed number of decimal places are denoted by X_j and we define residuals by (4.21) as before. Suppose that the exact roots x_j are related to the approximate roots by

$$x_j = X_j + \delta x_j, \quad (j = 1 \text{ to } n).$$

On substituting in (4.1) we readily find that the δx_j are the roots of the equations

$$\sum_{j=1}^{n} a_{ij} \delta x_j = b_i - \sum_{j=1}^{n} a_{ij} X_j = -r_i, \quad (i = 1 \text{ to } n). \quad (4.22)$$

The procedure is illustrated in the following example.

Ex. 4.4. *Find the accuracy of the roots obtained in Ex.* 4.2.

The residuals are found to be:

$$10^5 r_1 = \quad 0\cdot010, \quad 10^5 r_2 = -5\cdot072,$$
$$10^5 r_3 = -2\cdot512, \quad 10^5 r_4 = -2\cdot506.$$

The major part of the work involved in solving (4.22) has already been carried out in the table in Ex. 4.2 and it is necessary to calculate only one new b_i column. The results are almost exactly those given in Table 4.1:

$$\delta x_1 = 0\cdot0160, \quad \delta x_2 = 0\cdot0087,$$
$$\delta x_3 = 0\cdot0161, \quad \delta x_4 = -0\cdot0080_5.$$

Hence the roots in Ex. 4.2 are accurate to within one or two digits in the second decimal place.

In order to answer the question in (ii) above suppose that possible errors in a_{ij}, b_i are denoted by δa_{ij}, δb_i, and suppose that these alter the roots from x_j to $x_j + \delta x_j$. Then

$$\sum_{j=1}^{n} (a_{ij} + \delta a_{ij})(x_j + \delta x_j) = b_i + \delta b_i.$$

On neglecting second-order terms we find

$$\sum_{j=1}^{n} a_{ij} \delta x_j = \delta b_i - \sum_{j=1}^{n} \delta a_{ij} x_j, \quad (i = 1 \text{ to } n).$$

If $x_j = X_j + \varepsilon_j$, where the X_j are approximate roots, we obtain, again neglecting second-order terms,

$$\sum_{j=1}^{n} a_{ij} \delta x_j = \delta b_i - \sum_{j=1}^{n} \delta a_{ij} X_j = v_i, \text{ say.} \quad (4.23)$$

In many cases we can regard a solution as satisfactory if the error in the solution is comparable with the inherent error due to inexact coefficients. From (4.22) and (4.23) it is seen that a solution is satisfactory in this sense if the residuals $| r_i |$ are less than some average value (such as the root-mean-square value) of the magnitude of the quantities v_i deduced from the possible errors in coefficients. As an example consider the results in Ex. 4.2. The maximum residual has magnitude 5.10^{-5} (Ex. 4.4). The possible errors in coefficients can produce a maximum error of

$$ v_{max} \approx 5.10^{-5} \left[1 + \sum_{j=1}^{n} | X_j | \right] \approx 125.10^{-5}. $$

Statistically the error will be considerably less than this but it is unlikely that it will be reduced by the factor of 25 required to make the average $| v_i |$ comparable with the largest residual. Hence the solution obtained in Ex. 4.2 is satisfactory in the sense defined at the beginning of this paragraph. This type of result would seem to be the rule rather than the exception when the method of successive elimination is used, if the equations are scaled properly and one or two guarding figures are kept in the body of the calculation. The following example illustrates an empirical approach to the problem.

Ex. 4.5. *Alter the coefficients in the equations in Ex.* 4.2 *in the following way. Write the ten numbers* $-4(1)5$ *on slips of paper and for each* a_{ij} *and* b_i *pick one of the ten slips at random. Alter the corresponding coefficient by* 10^{-5} *times the number on the slip unless this number is 5, in which case alter the number by* 5.10^{-5} *if the end-digit is even and* -5.10^{-5} *if the end-digit is odd. Find the change produced in the roots* (4.18).

An experiment of this type gave

$$ 10^4 v_1 = -5 \cdot 23, \qquad 10^4 v_2 = 6 \cdot 98, $$
$$ 10^4 v_3 = -4 \cdot 60, \qquad 10^4 v_4 = 4 \cdot 46. $$
$$ \delta x_1 = -0 \cdot 0852, \qquad \delta x_2 = 0 \cdot 0447, $$
$$ \delta x_3 = 0 \cdot 0814, \qquad \delta x_4 = 0 \cdot 0398. $$

The errors in the solution in Ex. 4.2 (see Ex. 4.4) are about one-fifth of these.

We have now gone as far as we can, within the scope and limitations of this book, in considering the errors involved in solving simultaneous linear equations. An interesting theoretical treatment from a comparatively elementary point of view is given in *Modern Computing Methods*, H.M. Stationery Office, 2nd Edn. (1961), Chapter 5.

§ **4.5. A computer program for the method of successive elimination.**† Program 4.1 is a computer program for solving an $n \times n$ set of simultaneous linear equations by the method of § 4.2. The unknowns are eliminated in the order $x_1, x_2, \ldots x_n$. The pivot at each stage is chosen as the largest element in the first column of the appropriate array. When the statement labelled 12 is reached, this largest element has been determined and the appropriate rows have been interchanged so that the row containing the largest pivot is now the first row in the array from which the next unknown is to be eliminated. When statements 16 and 17 are completed the appropriate unknowns have been eliminated and the machine proceeds to eliminate the next unknown. The remainder of the program is concerned with back-substitution, computation of the determinant, and printing out the results. (It is advisable to print out some measure of the condition of the equations. The size of the determinant and the smallest pivot give some indication of whether the equations are badly conditioned. In order to save unnecessary printing it may be arranged that these are printed only if they fall below certain limits.) These hints should enable the reader to work through the program in detail, as an exercise. This will be more instructive than pages of further explanation.

† See also *Modern Computing Methods*, H.M. Stationery Office, 2nd Edition (1961), Chapter 2.

PROGRAM 4.1

LABEL	STATEMENT
	Read n, a_{ij} for $i = 1(1)\,n$ and $j = 1(1)\,n$, b_i for $i = 1(1)\,n$
	Print n, a_{ij} for $i = 1(1)\,n$ and $j = 1(1)\,n$, b_i for $i = 1(1)\,n$,
	Do up to 3 for $i = 1(1)\,n$
3	$a_{i,n+1} = b_i$
	Do up to 17 for $r = 1(1)\,n-1$
	$q = r$
4	$p = q$
5	If $q = n$ go to 10
	$q = q+1$
6	If $a_{pr} < a_{qr}$ go to 4
	Go to 5
10	Do up to 12 for $j = r\,(1)\,n+1$
	$c_j = a_{rj}$
	$a_{rj} = a_{pj}$
12	$a_{pj} = c_j$
16	Do up to 17 for $i = r+1(1)\,n$ and $j = r+1\,(1)\,n+1$
17	$a_{ij} = a_{ij} - (a_{ir}a_{rj})/a_{rr}$
	$x_n = a_{n,n+1}/a_{n,n}$
	Do up to 22 for $r = n-1(-1)1$
	$d = 0$
	Do up to 20 for $j = r+1(1)\,n$
20	$d = d + a_{rj}x_j$
22	$x_r = (a_{r,\,n+1} - d)/a_{rr}$
	$D = a_{11}$
	Do up to 25 for $i = 2(1)\,n$
25	$D = Da_{ii}$
	Print x_j for $j = 1(1)\,n$, a_{ii} for $i = 1(1)\,n$, D.
	Stop

Examples IV

(Examples for practice in numerical work can be derived from those in the text by rescaling the equations in Ex. 4.2 or by working the examples to a different number of decimal places. Some of the Examples V are relevant to this chapter.)

Ex. 4.6. Modify Program 4.1 so as to solve m sets of equations with the same set of coefficients a_{ij} but m different right-hand sides b_{ik} ($k = 1$ to m).

Ex. 4.7. Draw a flow-diagram for Program 4.1.

Ex. 4.8. Show that the number of multiplications involved in solving n simultaneous linear equations in n unknowns by the method of successive eliminations (§ 4.2) is of the order of $\frac{1}{3}n^3$. (This is an important result because the main labour in solving large sets of equations lies in the multiplications, so that the labour increases rapidly with the size of the set of equations. The same result holds for the compact elimination method of § 5.2 below.)

Ex. 4.9. Consider the set of equations

$$b_1 x_1 + c_1 x_2 = d_1,$$
$$a_j x_{j-1} + b_j x_j + c_j x_{j+1} = d_j, \quad (j = 2, 3, \ldots n-1),$$
$$a_n x_{n-1} + b_n x_n = d_n.$$

Show that the x_j can be determined from the formulae

$$g_1 = \frac{c_1}{b_1}, \quad g_j = \frac{c_j}{b_j - a_j g_{j-1}}, \quad (j = 2, 3, \ldots n-1),$$

$$h_1 = \frac{d_1}{b_1}, \quad h_j = \frac{d_j - a_j h_{j-1}}{b_j - a_j g_{j-1}}, \quad (j = 2, 3, \ldots n),$$

$$x_n = h_n, \quad x_j = h_j - g_j x_{j+1}, \quad (j = n-1, n-2, \ldots 1).$$

If $a_j < 0$, $b_j > 0$, $c_j < 0$, and $a_j + b_j + c_j \geqq 0$, show that $-1 \leqq g_j < 0$. (The number of operations involved is proportional to n compared with a number of operations proportional to n^3 for a general set of equations. The method can be justified from first principles but it is instructive to consider it from the point of view of the matrix decomposition in Ex. 5.11. Equations of the above type occur in connection with solution of the heat-conduction equation by implicit difference methods as in Ex. 11.2.)

H

CHAPTER V

MATRIX METHODS

§ 5.1. Matrix algebra. Matrices provide a useful method for systematising both the theoretical and the practical aspects of certain computing procedures, particularly in connection with automatic computers. We start Chapters V and VI with short summaries of the necessary theory,† to provide a guide for the beginner who might otherwise be confused by the mass of detail in text-books on matrices.

An $m \times n$ **matrix** A is simply a rectangular array of mn numbers, arranged in m rows and n columns. It is said to be of order " m by n " or " $m \times n$ ":

$$A = [a_{ij}] = \begin{bmatrix} a_{11} & a_{12} & \ldots & a_{1n} \\ a_{21} & a_{22} & \ldots & a_{2n} \\ & & \cdot & \cdot & \cdot \\ a_{m1} & a_{m2} & \ldots & a_{mn} \end{bmatrix}.$$

The (i, j)th element a_{ij} represents the element in the ith row and the jth column of the matrix.

Consider operations involving two matrices $A = [a_{ij}]$ and $B = [b_{ij}]$. Equality, addition, and subtraction are meaningful terms if and only if the matrices have the same number of rows and the same number of columns. If this

† Further information can be found in A. C. Aitken, *Determinants and Matrices*, Oliver and Boyd (1962).

is true then:

$$A = B \text{ if and only if } a_{ij} = b_{ij} \text{ for all } i, j.$$

$$A \pm B = [a_{ij} \pm b_{ij}].$$

This last equation means that the sum or difference of two matrices with equal numbers of rows and columns is the matrix such that any element is the sum or difference of the corresponding elements in A and B.

To multiply a matrix by a scalar, say k, each term of the matrix is multiplied by k:

$$kA = [ka_{ij}].$$

A matrix with only one row is called a **row matrix** (or a **row vector**) and a matrix with only one column is called a **column matrix** (or a **column vector**). The **scalar product** of a row matrix and a column matrix, taken in that order, is meaningful if and only if the row and column have the same number of terms, and then it consists of a single number defined as in the following example:

$$[x_1 \ x_2 \ \ldots \ x_n] \begin{bmatrix} y_1 \\ \vdots \\ y_n \end{bmatrix} = x_1 y_1 + x_2 y_2 + \ldots + x_n y_n.$$

Two matrices can be multiplied together if and only if the number of columns in the first is equal to the number of rows in the second. Then the element in the ith row and the jth column of the product is the scalar product of the ith row of the first matrix with the jth column of the second. If A is $m \times n$, B is $n \times p$, and

$$AB = C,$$

or

$$[a_{ij}][b_{jk}] = [c_{ik}],$$

then the rule determining c_{ik}, the elements of the product matrix C, is

$$c_{ik} = \sum_{j=1}^{n} a_{ij}b_{jk},$$

and C is $m \times p$. As an example,

$$\begin{bmatrix} a_{11} & a_{12} \\ a_{21} & a_{22} \\ a_{31} & a_{32} \end{bmatrix} \begin{bmatrix} b_{11} & b_{12} \\ b_{21} & b_{22} \end{bmatrix} = \begin{bmatrix} a_{11}b_{11}+a_{12}b_{21}, & a_{11}b_{12}+a_{12}b_{22} \\ a_{21}b_{11}+a_{22}b_{21}, & a_{21}b_{12}+a_{22}b_{22} \\ a_{31}b_{11}+a_{32}b_{21}, & a_{31}b_{12}+a_{32}b_{22} \end{bmatrix}.$$

The order in which matrices are multiplied together is obviously very important. The existence of the product AB is quite independent of the existence of BA and even if AB and BA both exist they will in general be unequal and there is no very useful connection between the two. In the product AB the matrix A is said to premultiply B, and B is said to postmultiply A.

Although the commutative law does not hold for multiplication ($AB \neq BA$ in general) the distributive and associative laws are true, e.g.

$$(A+B)C = AC+BC, \quad A(BC) = (AB)C = ABC.$$

It is useful to define certain special types of matrix. A matrix with the same number of rows and columns is called a **square** matrix. Associated with any square matrix A we have the determinant of the matrix:

$$\det A = \begin{vmatrix} a_{11} & \dots & a_{1n} \\ & \cdot \quad \cdot \quad \cdot & \\ a_{n1} & \dots & a_{nn} \end{vmatrix}.$$

If A and B are square matrices of the same order then (Aitken, loc. cit., p. 80)

$$\det AB = \det A \,.\, \det B. \tag{5.1}$$

A **diagonal** matrix $D = [d_{ij}]$ is a square matrix with all the d_{ij} zero except $d_{11}, d_{22}, \dots d_{nn}$ which are the elements along the **principal diagonal**, or the **diagonal elements**. A diagonal matrix all of whose diagonal elements are unity is called a **unit** matrix, and it is denoted by I. Clearly

$$AI = IA = A, \quad \det I = 1.$$

In matrix algebra I plays the same role as unity in ordinary algebra. The **transpose** A' of a matrix A is defined by the property that if A is an $m \times n$ matrix whose (i, j)th element is a_{ij} then A' is an $n \times m$ matrix whose (i, j)th element is a_{ji}, i.e. $[a_{ij}]' = [a_{ji}]$. A **symmetrical** matrix is a square matrix with $a_{ij} = a_{ji}$, i.e. $A' = A$.

§ 5.2. A compact elimination method for the solution of linear equations.

We describe a compact elimination method for the solution of linear equations which is essentially a telescoped version of a successive elimination method (see § 4.2 and Ex. 5.4). It is convenient to work in terms of matrices. We consider only 3×3 matrices when describing the theory, but the extension to the general case is direct. Lower and upper **triangular matrices** L, U are defined as matrices with zero elements above and below the principal diagonal, respectively:

$$L = \begin{bmatrix} l_{11} & 0 & 0 \\ l_{21} & l_{22} & 0 \\ l_{31} & l_{32} & l_{33} \end{bmatrix}, \qquad U = \begin{bmatrix} u_{11} & u_{12} & u_{13} \\ 0 & u_{22} & u_{23} \\ 0 & 0 & u_{33} \end{bmatrix}.$$

The set of linear simultaneous equations (4.1), for the case $n = 3$, can be expressed in matrix notation as

$$Ax = b$$

where

$$A = \begin{bmatrix} a_{11} & a_{12} & a_{13} \\ a_{21} & a_{22} & a_{23} \\ a_{31} & a_{32} & a_{33} \end{bmatrix}, \quad x = \begin{bmatrix} x_1 \\ x_2 \\ x_3 \end{bmatrix}, \quad b = \begin{bmatrix} b_1 \\ b_2 \\ b_3 \end{bmatrix}.$$

We first of all show that A can be expressed as the product of two matrices in the form $A = LU$ where L is a lower triangular matrix as defined above and U is an upper triangular matrix with units along the principal diagonal (i.e. $u_{ii} = 1$). (The diagonal elements of either L or U, but not of both, can be chosen arbitrarily.) We have

$$\begin{bmatrix} a_{11} & a_{12} & a_{13} \\ a_{21} & a_{22} & a_{23} \\ a_{31} & a_{32} & a_{33} \end{bmatrix} = \begin{bmatrix} l_{11} & 0 & 0 \\ l_{21} & l_{22} & 0 \\ l_{31} & l_{32} & l_{33} \end{bmatrix} \begin{bmatrix} 1 & u_{12} & u_{13} \\ 0 & 1 & u_{23} \\ 0 & 0 & 1 \end{bmatrix}$$

$$= \begin{bmatrix} l_{11} & l_{11}u_{12} & l_{11}u_{13} \\ l_{21} & l_{21}u_{12}+l_{22} & l_{21}u_{13}+l_{22}u_{23} \\ l_{31} & l_{31}u_{12}+l_{32} & l_{31}u_{13}+l_{32}u_{23}+l_{33} \end{bmatrix}.$$

On equating the individual elements in the first and last matrices we obtain equations which determine the elements of L and U. It is found that the elements of L and U can be determined as follows:

(a) The first column of L:

$$l_{11} = a_{11}, \quad l_{21} = a_{21}, \quad l_{31} = a_{31}.$$

(b) The first row of U:

$$u_{12} = a_{12}/l_{11}, \quad u_{13} = a_{13}/l_{11}.$$

(c) The second column of L:

$$l_{22} = a_{22}-l_{21}u_{12}, \quad l_{32} = a_{32}-l_{31}u_{12}.$$

(d) The second row of U:

$$u_{23} = (a_{23}-l_{21}u_{13})/l_{22}.$$

(e) The third column of L:

$$l_{33} = a_{33}-l_{31}u_{13}-l_{32}u_{23}.$$

The importance of doing the computations in the above order is that the quantities required to compute the value of an element at any stage of the calculation have already been computed at some previous stage. In hand computation it is of course important to evaluate sums of products in one machine operation, without intermediate recording.

Assuming that L, U are known, we can write $Ax = b$ as

$$LUx = b. \tag{5.2}$$

We introduce y defined by

$$y = Ux. \tag{5.3a}$$

Then (5.2) gives

$$Ly = b. \tag{5.3b}$$

Written out in full, equations (5.3a, b) are:

$$
\left.
\begin{aligned}
l_{11}y_1 \quad\quad\quad &= b_1 \\
l_{21}y_1 + l_{22}y_2 \quad &= b_2 \\
l_{31}y_1 + l_{32}y_2 + l_{33}y_3 &= b_3
\end{aligned}
\right\}
\quad
\left.
\begin{aligned}
x_1 + u_{12}x_2 + u_{13}x_3 &= y_1 \\
x_2 + u_{23}x_3 &= y_2 \\
x_3 &= y_3
\end{aligned}
\right\}
\tag{5.4}
$$

The values of y_1, y_2, y_3 can be computed in succession from the first set of equations and then x_1, x_2, x_3 can be computed in succession from the second set. If we solve the first set of equations in (5.4) for the y_i we see that

$$
\begin{aligned}
y_1 &= b_1/l_{11}, \\
y_2 &= (b_2 - l_{21}y_1)/l_{22}, \\
y_3 &= (b_3 - l_{31}y_1 - l_{32}y_2)/l_{33}.
\end{aligned}
\tag{5.5}
$$

Before considering the organisation of the calculation we show that numerical checks can be obtained in the following way. We first of all define the row sums

$$
\begin{aligned}
s_1 &= a_{11} + a_{12} + a_{13} + b_1, \\
s_2 &= a_{21} + a_{22} + a_{23} + b_2, \\
s_3 &= a_{31} + a_{32} + a_{33} + b_3.
\end{aligned}
$$

A little reflection shows that if the b_i on the right of the first set of equations in (5.4) are replaced by s_i, then the y_i on the right of the second set are replaced by the quantities

$$\Sigma_1 = 1 + u_{12} + u_{13} + y_1,$$
$$\Sigma_2 = 1 + u_{23} + y_2, \qquad (5.6a)$$
$$\Sigma_3 = 1 + y_3.$$

The same quantities are obtained if we follow the procedure used to derive the y_i:

$$\sigma_1 = s_1/l_{11},$$
$$\sigma_2 = (s_2 - l_{21}\sigma_1)/l_{22}, \qquad (5.6b)$$
$$\sigma_3 = (s_3 - l_{31}\sigma_1 - l_{32}\sigma_2)/l_{33}.$$

Algebraically the σ_i and Σ_i represent identical quantities but in numerical work they are computed in different ways so that the numerical values may differ slightly in the last significant figure due to round-off error. The approximate equality of the σ_i and Σ_i serves as an independent check on the calculation.

We now describe a practical procedure for carrying out the above method.† The symbols have been defined above except for the column check-sums (cf. § 4.2):

$$S_i = a_{1i} + a_{2i} + a_{3i} \quad (i = 1, 2, 3), \quad S_4 = b_1 + b_2 + b_3,$$
$$S = S_1 + S_2 + S_3 + S_4, \qquad\qquad s = s_1 + s_2 + s_3.$$

It is convenient to divide the calculation into three stages.

† P. D. Crout, Trans. Amer. Inst. Electr. Engrs. **60** (1941), 1235-40. Another layout is given in *Modern Computing Methods*, H.M. Stationery Office, 2nd Edition (1961), Chapter 1. Which of these layouts is recommended depends on personal preference.

(i) Write down the *original matrix* with check sums:

$$a_{11} \quad a_{12} \quad a_{13} \quad b_1 \quad (s_1)$$
$$a_{21} \quad a_{22} \quad a_{23} \quad b_2 \quad (s_2)$$
$$a_{31} \quad a_{32} \quad a_{33} \quad b_3 \quad (s_3)$$
$$(S_1) \quad (S_2) \quad (S_3) \quad (S_4) \quad (S = s).$$

(ii) Write down an *auxiliary matrix*. The method of deriving this matrix is given below. It may be noted at this point that the u_{ij}, y_i, and σ_i are all determined by following exactly the same rule (cf. (b), (d), (5.5), and (5.6b) above, and the rule given in the paragraph preceding Ex. 5.1 below).

$$l_{11} \quad u_{12} \quad u_{13} \quad y_1 \quad (\sigma_1 \approx \Sigma_1)$$
$$l_{21} \quad l_{22} \quad u_{23} \quad y_2 \quad (\sigma_2 \approx \Sigma_2)$$
$$l_{31} \quad l_{32} \quad l_{33} \quad y_3 \quad (\sigma_3 \approx \Sigma_3).$$

(iii) Obtain the unknowns by back-substitution in the second set of equations in (5.4) and apply the final check:

$$S_4' = S_1 x_1 + S_2 x_2 + S_3 x_3 \approx S_4.$$

The elements of the auxiliary matrix are written down in the following order:

(a) Elements of the first column, l_{i1}.
(b) Elements of the first row to the right of the diagonal, u_{1j}, y_1, σ_1. Then apply a check:

$$\Sigma_1 = 1 + u_{12} + u_{13} + y_1 \approx \sigma_1.$$

(c) Elements of the second column on and below the diagonal, l_{i2}.
(d) Elements of the second row to the right of the diagonal, u_{2j}, y_2, σ_2. (Notice that Σ_1 not σ_1 is

used to compute σ_2 (cf. Ex. 4.2).) Then apply the check:

$$\Sigma_2 = 1 + u_{23} + y_2 \approx \sigma_2.$$

(e) Elements of the third column on and below the diagonal, l_{33}.

(f) Elements of the third row to the right of the diagonal, y_3, σ_3. (Note that Σ_1, Σ_2 not σ_1, σ_2 are used to compute σ_3.) Then apply the check:

$$\Sigma_3 = 1 + y_3 \approx \sigma_3.$$

The elements of the auxiliary matrix are determined by the following general rule: Each element on or below the diagonal is equal to the corresponding element in the original matrix minus the sum of products of elements in its row with corresponding elements in its column, in the auxiliary matrix, where these products involve only previously computed elements. Each element to the right of the diagonal is obtained by exactly the same rule except that finally we divide by the diagonal term in the same row. This last part of the rule applies to the u_{ij}, y_i, and σ_i but it does not of course apply to the checks Σ_i which are defined as in (5.6a). If the matrix A is symmetrical, labour can be saved by noting that each element u_{ij} of U is equal to the symmetrically situated element l_{ji} of L divided by the diagonal element l_{ii}.

Ex. 5.1. *Apply the above method to the equations:*

$$\begin{aligned}
x_1 + 4x_2 + x_3 + 3x_4 &= 1, \\
- x_2 + 3x_3 + x_4 &= -4, \\
3x_1 + x_2 + 6x_3 - 10x_4 &= -11, \\
x_1 - 2x_2 + 5x_3 &= 1.
\end{aligned} \qquad (5.7)$$

Show that the auxiliary matrix, including check columns, is

1	4	1	3	1	(10)
0	-1	-3	-1	4	(1)
3	-11	-30	1	-1	(1)
1	-6	-14	5	2	(3),

and deduce the solution

$$x_1 = 10, \quad x_2 = -3, \quad x_3 = -3, \quad x_4 = 2.$$

Ex. 5.2. *Solve the equations of Ex.* 4.2 *by the above method*
The auxiliary matrix is (omitting the check column)

0·5400	0·969 07	0·807 04	0·670 74	2·410 19
0·5233	0·280 09	$-0·214\ 66$	0·623 73	$-3·640\ 80$
0·4358	$-0·060\ 12$	0·023 49	1·808 86	0·057 65
0·3622	0·174 70	0·042 49	0·008 93	$-6·357\ 51$

Roots: $x_1 = -5·3717$, $x_2 = 2·8055$, $x_3 = 11·5575$, $x_4 = -6·3575$.
Errors: $\delta x_1 = -0·0151$, $\delta x_2 = 0·0082$, $\delta x_3 = 0·0154$, $\delta x_4 = -0·0078$.

It is seen that the errors are almost exactly the same as those obtained by the method of successive elimination in § 4.2 (see Table 4.1). Theoretically we should expect the compact method to be slightly more accurate than the method of successive elimination since there are fewer round-off errors.

Ex. 5.3. *Show that the compact method gives the following results for scaled equations in Ex.* 4.3:

Roots: $x_1 = -5·3715$, $x_2 = 2·8054$, $x_3 = 11·5575$, $x_4 = -6·3574$.
Errors: $\delta x_1 = -0·0153$, $\delta x_2 = 0·0083$, $\delta x_3 = 0·0154$, $\delta x_4 = -0·0079$.

Ex. 5.4. *Derive the compact method corresponding to the method of successive elimination of* § 4.2, *in the following way, from equations* (4.4)-(4.10).
We have $e_4 = d_4 - l_{43}d_3$. In this expression substitute

for d_4 in terms of c_4, and then for c_4 in terms of b_4 to find

$$e_4 = b_4 - l_{41}b_1 - l_{42}c_2 - l_{43}d_3.$$

Similarly show that all the terms in (4.5), (4.8), (4.10) can be expressed in terms of quantities which occur in these equations, the original matrix, and the l_{ij}. Show that a similar result holds for the l_{ij}. Hence it is unnecessary to record the quantities in the square brackets in (4.6), (4.7), (4.9). Show that the resulting formulae are in fact exactly those involved in solving $Ax = b$ by decomposing A in the form $A = LU$, where L has units along the principal diagonal.

In the compact method described above we have arranged that it is U which has units along the diagonal instead of L. Show that this is a condensed form of the method of successive elimination in which, for instance, we divide the row of quantities a_{1j}, b_1, s_1 in (4.4) by a_{11} instead of dividing the column a_{i1} by a_{11} and similarly for the other arrays.

There are various methods of choosing the diagonal elements in L and U, and arranging the methods of successive elimination and compact elimination. The precise variant which is chosen is largely a matter of personal preference.

§ 5.3. The inverse matrix.

Suppose that, given an $n \times n$ matrix A, there exists a matrix Z such that

$$AZ = I.$$

Then it is possible to show that $ZA = I$. The matrix Z is called the **inverse** of A and it is usually denoted by A^{-1}. When A^{-1} exists we have

$$A^{-1}A = AA^{-1} = I. \tag{5.8}$$

From this relation, using (5.1), we have

$$\det A . \det A^{-1} = 1.$$

Hence a necessary condition for the existence of the inverse of A is that det $A \neq 0$. If this is true then the matrix A is said to be **non-singular,** but if det $A = 0$ the matrix A is said to be **singular** and in this case the inverse does not exist.

Instead of dividing by matrices we multiply by the inverse matrix. As an example consider the simultaneous linear equations (4.1) which in matrix notation are

$$Ax = b. \tag{5.9}$$

We assume that the determinant of the coefficients is non-zero so that a unique solution of the equations exists, and the inverse matrix also exists. To solve (5.9) we wish to remove A from the left-hand side. Premultiply both sides by A^{-1}:

$$A^{-1}Ax = A^{-1}b.$$

On using (5.8) we have

$$x = A^{-1}b. \tag{5.10}$$

One practical procedure for the determination of the inverse matrix is obvious from its definition. Denote the jth column of A^{-1} by z_j and let d_j denote the $n \times 1$ column matrix whose elements are zero except for the jth element which is unity. Then $AA^{-1} = I$ gives

$$Az_j = d_j, \quad (j = 1, 2, \ldots n).$$

These are just n sets of simultaneous linear equations with n different right-hand sides of simple form, but the same coefficient matrix on the left. They can be solved by extending any method for solution of a single set of equations. As an example consider the extension of the compact method of § 5.2. The " original matrix " will appear as follows:

$$
\begin{array}{cccccc}
a_{11} & a_{12} & a_{13} & 1\cdot0 & 0 & 0 & (s_1) \\
a_{21} & a_{22} & a_{23} & 0 & 1\cdot0 & 0 & (s_2) \quad (5.11) \\
a_{31} & a_{32} & a_{33} & 0 & 0 & 1\cdot0 & (s_3) \\
(S_1) & (S_2) & (S_3) & (1\cdot0) & (1\cdot0) & (1\cdot0) & (S = s).
\end{array}
$$

There is still only one check column, obtained by adding all the elements in the corresponding rows. The " auxiliary matrix " will be of the form

$$
\begin{array}{cccccc}
l_{11} & u_{12} & u_{13} & m_{11} & 0 & 0 & (\sigma_1 \approx \Sigma_1) \\
l_{21} & l_{22} & u_{23} & m_{21} & m_{22} & 0 & (\sigma_2 \approx \Sigma_2) \\
l_{31} & l_{32} & l_{33} & m_{31} & m_{32} & m_{33} & (\sigma_3 \approx \Sigma_3).
\end{array}
$$

In the position occupied by the unit matrix I in the original matrix there is a lower triangular matrix with elements m_{ij}. The calculation can be completed by forming a **back-substitution matrix** of the following form:

$$
\begin{array}{cccccc}
1 & u_{12} & u_{13} & A_{11} & A_{12} & A_{13} \\
0 & 1 & u_{23} & A_{21} & A_{22} & A_{23} \\
0 & 0 & 1 & A_{31} & A_{32} & A_{33}.
\end{array}
$$

The A_{ij} are the required elements of A^{-1}. Checks are given by

$$
S_1 A_{1j} + S_2 A_{2j} + S_3 A_{3j} = 1, \quad (j = 1, 2, 3).
$$

The square matrix on the left of the back-substitution matrix is simply the upper triangular matrix U. The elements A_{ij} are obtained in the order: last row from left to right, second last row from left to right, and so on. The last row is the same as the corresponding part of the last row in the auxiliary matrix. The second last row is given by the formula

$$
A_{2j} = m_{2j} - u_{23} A_{3j}, \quad (j = 1, 2, 3),
$$

where of course m_{23} is taken to be zero. The general rule for the element A_{ij} is: Any element is given by the corresponding element in the auxiliary matrix less the sum of products of previously computed elements in its column and corresponding elements in its row in the U matrix. The ith element in its column is taken with the ith element in the row of the U matrix.

The method extends directly to the general $n \times n$ case. It is seen that the amount of labour involved in finding an inverse matrix is about three times the work involved in solving a single set of equations, independent of the value of n.

Ex. 5.5. *Find A^{-1} for the matrix A of the equations in Ex. 4.2.*

Part of the auxiliary matrix has already been given in Ex. 5.2.

$$A^{-1} = \begin{bmatrix} 399 \cdot 8 & -213 \cdot 3 & -401 \cdot 7 & 198 \cdot 2 \\ -213 \cdot 3 & 120 \cdot 2 & 214 \cdot 1 & -113 \cdot 3 \\ -401 \cdot 7 & 214 \cdot 1 & 409 \cdot 0 & -202 \cdot 6 \\ 198 \cdot 2 & -113 \cdot 3 & -202 \cdot 6 & 112 \cdot 0 \end{bmatrix}.$$

Ex. 5.6. *Solve the equations in Ex. 4.2 by the formula $x = A^{-1}b$, using the inverse matrix found in Ex. 5.5.*

Roots: $x_1 = -5 \cdot 3822$, $x_2 = 2 \cdot 8157$, $x_3 = 11 \cdot 5627$, $x_4 = -6 \cdot 3607$.
Errors: $\delta x_1 = -0 \cdot 0046$, $\delta x_2 = -0 \cdot 0020$, $\delta x_3 = 0 \cdot 0102$, $\delta x_4 = -0 \cdot 0046$.

Note that in this example the individual terms of A^{-1} are large compared with the final roots. This indicates that the equations are ill-conditioned since in the sum of products required to form the roots large terms cancel to give small end-results. On the other hand the degree of ill-conditioning is not excessive.

We make the following comments in connection with the discussion of pivots and scaling in § 4.3. The elements of

A^{-1} in Ex. 5.5 are comparable with each other in size.
Since we are using fixed-point working and the elements of
A are comparable this means that the errors of the elements
of A^{-1} should be comparable.   If there is considerable
variation in the sizes of the largest elements in the rows
(or columns) of an inverse we have to be careful that we are
not losing accuracy unnecessarily in the sense that the
accuracy of the inverse could be improved by scaling the
original matrix.   In the method described above for in-
verting a matrix we can obtain various choices of pivots by
rearranging the rows and columns of the original matrix.
Whatever choice of pivots is used the inverse of the last is
always an element of the inverse matrix.   If the last pivot
is small then at least one element of the inverse matrix is
large, and the equations are to this extent ill-conditioned.
This is one way of seeing that the size of the last pivot has
a second-order effect on accuracy.

The condition of the equations $Ax = b$ depends on the
matrix A and not on b.   The equations are ill-conditioned
if, when we check that $A^{-1}A$ is equal to I, then terms large
compared with unity have cancelled to give (approximately)
units along the principal diagonal and zeros elsewhere.

If B is a matrix such that $BA \approx I$ then we say that B
is an approximate **left-inverse** of A, and similarly if $AC \approx I$
the matrix C is an approximate **right-inverse** of A.   Due to
ill-conditioning, even if $AC \approx I$ the product CA may not be
a good approximation to I.   As an example consider

$$A = \begin{bmatrix} 1 \cdot 00 & 1 \cdot 00 \\ 1 \cdot 00 & 0 \cdot 99 \end{bmatrix}, \qquad C = \begin{bmatrix} -89 & 100 \\ 90 & -100 \end{bmatrix}.$$

Then

$$AC = \begin{bmatrix} 1 \cdot 0 & 0 \cdot 0 \\ 0 \cdot 1 & 1 \cdot 0 \end{bmatrix}, \qquad CA = \begin{bmatrix} 11 & 10 \\ -10 & -9 \end{bmatrix}.$$

A good right-inverse may not be a good left-inverse, and
conversely.   The situation in numerical work is quite

different from the situation in the algebraic theory where the left- and right-inverses are the same.

We conclude this chapter by expressing in terms of matrices the discussion at the end of § 4.4 concerning accuracy when solving linear equations. We define a column matrix of residues, r, by the equation

$$r = AX - b,$$

where X is an approximate set of roots. If the exact roots x are related to the approximate roots by the equation

$$x = X + \delta x,$$

where δx is a column matrix of errors, we readily find

$$A\delta x = -r, \quad \text{i.e. } \delta x = -A^{-1}r. \tag{5.12}$$

This is the matrix form of (4.22).

If errors in the coefficients are given by

$$\delta A = [\delta a_{ij}], \quad \delta b = [\delta b_i],$$

and the corresponding new roots are denoted by $x + \delta x$, we have

$$(A + \delta A)(x + \delta x) = b + \delta b.$$

On neglecting the second-order term $\delta A \delta x$ we find

$$\delta x = A^{-1}(\delta b - \delta A x). \tag{5.13}$$

This is the matrix form of (4.23).

When using (5.12) it is essential to evaluate the residuals r to the number of significant figures required in δx, and since the residuals are small this may mean using a large number of decimal places when calculating the residuals. On the other hand A^{-1} need only be known to the number of significant figures required in δx, which may mean that only an approximate determination of A^{-1} is required. If an approximate value of A^{-1} is known then the roots of $Ax = b$ can be evaluated as accurately as required by the

I

iteration

$$x_0 = (A^{-1})_{\text{approx}}\, b,$$

$$x_{s+1} = x_s - (A^{-1})_{\text{approx}}\, r_s, \quad (s = 0, 1, 2, \ldots), \quad (5.14)$$

where x_s is the sth approximation to x. The residuals must be evaluated with the appropriate accuracy at each stage. This is an illustration of the principle that in an iterative procedure it is often possible to use approximations in certain parts of the computation, provided that the requisite accuracy is maintained in certain vital parts of the calculation.

Ex. 5.7. *Check the results of Exs. 4.4, 4.5 by using the inverse matrix in Ex. 5.5 in conjunction with (5.12), (5.13).*

When working with simultaneous linear equations it often happens, as in Ex. 5.7 compared with Exs. 4.4, 4.5, that we can either evaluate $z = A^{-1}d$ if A^{-1} is available, or we can solve $Az = d$ where the major part of the work has already been done since another set of equations $Ax = b$ has already been solved. To some extent the choice is a matter of personal preference. In hand computing it may be preferable to work with A^{-1} since multiplication by A^{-1} is rather more straightforward than adding an extra column to an auxiliary matrix and back-substituting. Also the size of the terms in A^{-1} gives some indication of the condition of the matrix. When using a computer it may be preferable to solve an extra set of equations, but this of course depends on what is stored inside the machine.

Examples V

Ex. 5.8. Write a computer program (or a flow-diagram) for the solution of linear equations by the compact method of § 5.2.

Ex. 5.9. Write a computer program (or a flow-diagram) for the inversion of a matrix using
   (i) the compact method explained in connection with (5.11),
   (ii) the successive elimination method of § 4.2 (compare Program 4.1).

Ex. 5.10. A compact method which is sometimes useful when it is desired to avoid small pivots is the square-root method in which we choose $l_{ii} = u_{ii}$ in the decomposition $A = LU$. Work out the details and show that when A is symmetrical U is equal to the transpose of L. Apply the method to the example in Ex. 4.2 and show that the errors are about two-thirds of those by the method of Ex. 4.2 (Table 4.1). (The labour involved in taking square roots is justified only if otherwise the pivots become undesirably small in the sense discussed in § 4.3.)

Ex. 5.11. Show that the band or tridiagonal matrix A defined by
$$a_{ij} = 0 \text{ for } |i-j| > 1$$
can be decomposed in the form LU where L is a lower diagonal matrix with $l_{ij} = 0$ for $i-j>1$ and U is an upper diagonal matrix with $u_{ii} = 1$ and $u_{ij} = 0$ for $j-i>1$. Find L and U for
$$A = \begin{bmatrix} 2 & -1 & 0 & 0 \\ -1 & 2 & -1 & 0 \\ 0 & -1 & 2 & -1 \\ 0 & 0 & -1 & 2 \end{bmatrix}.$$
Consider the procedure in Ex. 4.9 from the point of view of the compact elimination method of § 5.2.

Ex. 5.12. Find the exact inverse of the matrix A given at the end of Ex. 5.11, using the compact method explained in connection with (5.11), expressing all non-integral numbers as fractions instead of using decimals.

Ex. 5.13. Show that $(AB)' = B'A'$, and $(AB)^{-1} = B^{-1}A^{-1}$ if both inverses exist.

Ex. 5.14. Evaluate det A, the determinant of the coefficients a_{ij}, for the example in Ex. 4.2, to four significant figures. (The pivots in Ex. 4.2 where five decimals were carried in the intermediate calculations give det $A \approx 0\cdot3173 \times 10^{-4}$. A similar calculation carrying six decimals gives det $A \approx 0\cdot3167 \times 10^{-4}$. Keeping one extra decimal place does not mean that the error is reduced by exactly one decimal place, since round-off errors occur at random. But the results indicate that the last result is correct to one digit in the fourth significant figure. How could the accuracy be checked if you were using a digital computer?)

Ex. 5.15. Suppose that we are given m pairs of points (x_j, y_j) and it is required to represent the numbers y_j approximately by a relation of the form $y_j \approx f(x_j)$ where

$$f(x) = z_1 f_1(x) + z_2 f_2(x) + \ldots + z_n f_n(x), \quad (n < m),$$

where the $f_i(x)$ are known functions and the z_i are constants which are to be determined. This procedure is known as **curve-fitting**. We set

$$R_s = \sum_{i=1}^{n} z_i f_i(x_s) - y_s, \quad (s = 1 \text{ to } m),$$

and determine the z_i by the **principle of least squares**. We minimise

$$\sum_{s=1}^{m} R_s^2 = \sum_{s=1}^{m} \left\{ \sum_{i=1}^{n} z_i f_i(x_s) - y_s \right\}^2.$$

Partial differentiation with respect to $z_j (j = 1 \text{ to } n)$ gives n equations in n unknowns which can be written, in matrix form,

$$A'Az = A'y,$$

where

$$A = [a_{ij}] = [f_j(x_i)], \quad z = [z_i], \quad y = [y_i],$$

and A is $m \times n$, z is $n \times 1$, y is $m \times 1$.

These equations can be badly conditioned, especially if the points (x_j, y_j) tend to group in clusters. In such cases it may be advisable to replace a cluster of say p points by a single point at the centre of gravity of the cluster, repeated p times.

Fit a quadratic to the following points:

x_j	0·52	1·22	2·06	3·47	4·00	4·60
y_j	2·90	1·72	1·20	2·00	2·61	4·05

Ex. 5.16. Show that the inverse of the matrix of coefficients of the equations (5.7) is

$$A^{-1} = \tfrac{1}{150}\begin{bmatrix} 27 & -271 & -19 & 180 \\ 21 & 67 & 13 & -60 \\ 3 & 81 & 9 & -30 \\ 12 & -26 & -14 & 30 \end{bmatrix}.$$

Ex. 5.17. The effect on the solution of a set of simultaneous linear equations $Ax = b$ of modifying one of the coefficients a_{ij} can be analysed in the following way. Suppose that we know $A^{-1} = [A_{ij}]$ and we wish to solve $(A+D)x = b$ where D is an $n \times n$ matrix with typical element d_{ij} such that d_{ij} is zero unless $i = r, j = s$, i.e. d_{rs} is the only non-zero element of D. Then

$$(I+A^{-1}D)x = A^{-1}b.$$

If x^* is the solution of $Ax^* = b$ show that

$$x_s = \frac{x_s^*}{1 + A_{sr}d_{rs}}, \quad x_j = x_j^* - A_{jr}d_{rs}x_s, \quad (j \neq s).$$

Show that the solution of (5.7) with the second equation replaced by

$$-x_2 + 2x_3 + x_4 = -4$$

is given by

$$23x_1 = 501, \quad 23x_2 = -136, \quad 23x_3 = -150, \quad 23x_4 = 72.$$

CHAPTER VI

EIGENVALUES AND EIGENVECTORS

§ **6.1. Introduction.** Many of the applications of matrices involve eigenvalues and eigenvectors. To introduce the ideas which are involved we discuss a simple physical example. Further applications occur, for instance, in connection with the principal axes of a quadric, and the principal moments of inertia of a solid body.† The reader who does not find physical examples illuminating can start with the mathematical definition (6.3) below.

Consider three particles, each of mass m, at equal distances l along an elastic string of length $4l$, where the string is fixed at both ends. If the particles execute small transverse vibrations under no external forces, the equations of motion are

$$m \frac{d^2X_1}{dt^2} = -\frac{TX_1}{l} + \frac{T(X_2 - X_1)}{l},$$

$$m \frac{d^2X_2}{dt^2} = -\frac{T(X_2 + X_1)}{l} + \frac{T(X_3 - X_2)}{l},$$

$$m \frac{d^2X_3}{dt^2} = -\frac{T(X_3 - X_2)}{l} - \frac{TX_3}{l},$$

† See W. H. McCrea, *Analytical Geometry of Three Dimensions*, Oliver and Boyd (1960) and D. E. Rutherford, *Classical Mechanics*, Oliver and Boyd (1960). For mathematical properties of eigenvalues and eigenvectors (Latent roots and vectors) see A. C. Aitken, *Determinants and Matrices*, Oliver and Boyd (1962).

where X_1, X_2, X_3 are the displacements of the three particles and T is the tension in the string. If all quantities vary sinusoidally with time we can set

$$X_r = x_r e^{i\omega t}, \quad (r = 1, 2, 3).$$

Then the above equations become

$$
\begin{aligned}
(2-\lambda)x_1 - \qquad x_2 \qquad\qquad &= 0, \\
-x_1 + (2-\lambda)x_2 - \qquad x_3 &= 0, \qquad (6.1) \\
-x_2 + (2-\lambda)x_3 &= 0,
\end{aligned}
$$

where $\lambda = \omega^2 ml/T$. This is a homogeneous set of simultaneous linear algebraic equations which in general possesses only the trivial solution $x_1 = x_2 = x_3 = 0$. However, non-zero solutions will exist for special values of λ. From Cramer's rule (4.2) for the solution of linear equations in terms of the ratios of determinants we deduce that a necessary condition for the existence of a non-zero solution of (6.1) is that the determinant of the coefficients is zero:

$$
\begin{vmatrix}
2-\lambda & -1 & 0 \\
-1 & 2-\lambda & -1 \\
0 & -1 & 2-\lambda
\end{vmatrix} = 0. \qquad (6.2)
$$

By expanding this determinant we obtain a cubic equation in λ which can be solved to give the three special values of λ for which non-zero solutions of (6.1) exist, namely

$$\lambda = 2-\sqrt{2}, \quad 2, \quad 2+\sqrt{2}.$$

If in (6.1) we set $\lambda = 2-\sqrt{2}$ then we find that the resulting equations have a solution $x_1 = C$, $x_2 = C\sqrt{2}$, $x_3 = C$, where C is any arbitrary constant. The physical meaning of this is that corresponding to $\lambda = 2-\sqrt{2}$ there is a free vibration of angular frequency ω given by $\omega^2 = T(2-\sqrt{2})/ml$, and corresponding to this frequency of vibration there is a mode of oscillation such that the ratios $x_1 : x_2 : x_3$ are given by $1 : \sqrt{2} : 1$. Similarly

for $\lambda = 2$, $\qquad x_1 : x_2 : x_3 = 1 : 0 : -1$,

for $\lambda = 2 + \sqrt{2}$, $\quad x_1 : x_2 : x_3 = 1 : -\sqrt{2} : 1$.

This analysis shows that there are three and only three frequencies of free vibration. Corresponding to each of these frequencies there exists a solution of equations (6.1) which gives the corresponding mode of oscillation. The modes for this particular case are shown graphically in Fig. 6.1. The reader should visualise these modes physically.

We now express these ideas in more precise mathematical terminology. If A is an $n \times n$ matrix then, generalising (6.1), we consider the equations

$$(A - \lambda I)x = 0, \quad \text{or} \quad Ax = \lambda x. \tag{6.3}$$

From Cramer's rule (4.2) these equations possess only the trivial solution $x = 0$ unless the determinant of the co-efficients is zero:

$$\det (A - \lambda I) = \begin{vmatrix} a_{11} - \lambda & a_{12} & \dots & a_{1n} \\ a_{21} & a_{22} - \lambda & \dots & a_{2n} \\ & \cdot & \cdot & \cdot \\ a_{n1} & a_{n2} & \dots & a_{nn} - \lambda \end{vmatrix} = 0. \tag{6.4}$$

This is a polynomial equation in λ. The roots of this algebraic equation are special values of λ for which the simultaneous equations (6.3) possess non-zero solutions. They are called the **eigenvalues** of the matrix A and will be denoted by λ_i ($i = 1$ to n). The λ_i are sometimes called latent roots, characteristic roots, or proper values. Corresponding to each of the λ_i there will be a solution of (6.3) of the form Cx_i where x_i is a non-zero vector and C is an arbitrary constant. These solutions are called the **eigenvectors** (or latent vectors, characteristic vectors, proper vectors). We have

$$Ax_i = \lambda_i x_i. \tag{6.5}$$

We now deduce some properties of the eigenvalues and eigenvectors for the special case where the a_{ij} are real and

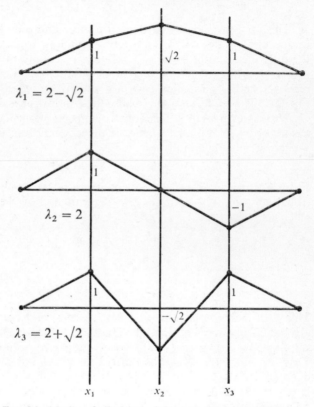

$\lambda_1 = 2 - \sqrt{2}$

$\lambda_2 = 2$

$\lambda_3 = 2 + \sqrt{2}$

FIG. 6.1 Modes of vibration of three particles on a string

A is symmetrical. We first of all show that then the eigenvalues and eigenvectors are real. In the general case, since the λ_i are roots of an algebraic equation, the eigenvalues may be complex and therefore the elements of x_i

may be complex. Denote by $\bar{x}_i$ a vector whose elements are the complex conjugates of those of x_i. The transpose $\bar{x}'_i$ of $\bar{x}_i$ is a row vector whose pth element is the pth element of the column vector $\bar{x}_i$. Multiplication of (6.5) by $\bar{x}'_i$ gives:

$$\lambda_i = \bar{x}'_i A x_i / \bar{x}'_i x_i. \tag{6.6}$$

(We adopt the convention that if y, z are $n \times 1$ column vectors with elements y_i, z_i, ($i = 1$ to n), then $y'z$ denotes a scalar defined by

$$y'z = y_1 z_1 + y_2 z_2 + \cdots + y_n z_n,$$

the **inner product** of y and z. Strictly speaking $y'z$ is a 1×1 matrix and the inner product should be denoted by some special symbol such as $x.y$ or (x, y) but no confusion will arise from our usage.) On writing $\bar{x}'_i x_i$ and $\bar{x}'_i A x_i$ in full it is seen, on using the assumption that A is symmetrical, that both of these expressions are real. Hence the λ_i are real. Corresponding to each of the λ_i, equations (6.3) will possess a solution of the form Cx_i where the elements of x_i are real. From now on we can therefore drop the bars.

If we multiply (6.5) by x'_j, ($j \neq i$), write down the corresponding expression with i and j interchanged, and subtract the two expressions, we obtain, since $x'_j A x_i = x'_i A x_j$ and $x'_j x_i = x'_j x_i$,

$$(\lambda_i - \lambda_j) x'_j x_i = 0, \quad (i \neq j).$$

We shall assume that the eigenvalues are distinct, i.e. $\lambda_i \neq \lambda_j$. Then

$$x'_j x_i = 0, \quad (i \neq j). \tag{6.7}$$

If this equation is satisfied the vectors x_i and x_j are said to be **orthogonal** and the eigenvectors x_i form an **orthogonal set** of vectors. Since the elements of an eigenvector are derived from homogeneous equations these elements can be multiplied by an arbitrary constant. It is usually convenient to adjust the size of the elements by some standard rule. This procedure is called **normalisation** and it can be done in various ways. We shall use two kinds of normalisation in this chapter:

(i) The eigenvectors can be normalised so that the numerically largest element of each eigenvector is unity.

(ii) An eigenvector x_i with elements d_1, d_2, ... d_n can be normalised so that

$$x_i' x_i = d_1^2 + d_2^2 + \ldots + d_n^2 = 1.$$

In this case we say that the eigenvectors are normalised to have unit length.

If a set of vectors is such that it is impossible to find constants α_i, not all of which are zero, such that

$$\alpha_1 x_1 + \alpha_2 x_2 + \ldots + \alpha_n x_n = 0, \qquad (6.8)$$

then the vectors are said to be **linearly independent**. A useful deduction from this definition is that if a relation of the form (6.8) holds between linearly independent vectors then $\alpha_1 = \alpha_2 = \ldots = \alpha_n = 0$. Orthogonal vectors are linearly independent for, if a relation of the form (6.8) exists, we see on multiplying by x_i' that $\alpha_i = 0$ and this holds for all i.

An arbitrary $n \times 1$ vector u can be expressed uniquely as a sum of multiples of n orthogonal $n \times 1$ vectors:

$$u = a_1 x_1 + a_2 x_2 + \ldots + a_n x_n, \qquad (6.9)$$

where the a_i are suitable constants. For if the a_i are regarded as unknowns then (6.9) is an $n \times n$ set of simultaneous linear equations for the a_i. The determinant of the coefficients is non-zero since otherwise the sum of certain multiples of the columns of the determinant would be zero, i.e. (6.8) would be true, but we have just shown that this is impossible.

Hence the determinant of the coefficients is non-zero, and values for the a_i exist and are unique. In fact we can easily write down the solution explicitly since multiplication of (6.9) by x_i' gives

$$a_i = x_i'u/x_i'x_i.$$

Ex. 6.1. *From the results for the problem discussed at the beginning of § 6.1 deduce that the matrix*

$$A = \begin{bmatrix} 2 & -1 & 0 \\ -1 & 2 & -1 \\ 0 & -1 & 2 \end{bmatrix} \qquad (6.10)$$

has eigenvalues $\lambda_1 = 2-\sqrt{2}$, $\lambda_2 = 2$, $\lambda_3 = 2+\sqrt{2}$, *with corresponding eigenvectors, normalised to unit length,*

$$x_1 = \begin{bmatrix} \tfrac{1}{2} \\ \tfrac{1}{2}\sqrt{2} \\ \tfrac{1}{2} \end{bmatrix}, \quad x_2 = \begin{bmatrix} \tfrac{1}{2}\sqrt{2} \\ 0 \\ -\tfrac{1}{2}\sqrt{2} \end{bmatrix}, \quad x_3 = \begin{bmatrix} \tfrac{1}{2} \\ -\tfrac{1}{2}\sqrt{2} \\ \tfrac{1}{2} \end{bmatrix}.$$

It is readily verified that $x_i'x_j = 0$, $(i \neq j)$.

§ 6.2. An iterative method for finding the largest eigenvalue.

In the last section we obtained the eigenvalues for a particular example by direct expansion of the determinant (6.2). This will not be a very efficient method for determinants of large order. In this section we discuss an iterative method for finding the largest eigenvalue of a general $n \times n$ matrix.

We assume that the matrix is symmetrical and real, since this is the case covered by the theory in § 6.1. The eigenvalues are then real, and we shall assume that there is one eigenvalue of maximum modulus. An extension to the case where there are two eigenvalues of the same modulus, but opposite signs, is given in Ex. 6.7. The method given in this section can be extended to other cases (but these will not be examined in detail):

(a) If the matrix is real but unsymmetrical, it is necessary to introduce biorthogonal functions as in Ex. 6.9. The method given in this section applies if there is one eigenvalue of largest modulus. In this case the eigenvalue of largest modulus will automatically be real, since, if the matrix is real, complex eigenvalues always occur in conjugate pairs. A method for dealing with complex conjugate dominant eigenvalues is given in Ex. 6.8.

(b) If the matrix has complex elements, it is relatively easy to extend the theory in § 6.1 to the case of a Hermitian matrix, where the elements are complex, but $\bar{a}_{ji} = a_{ij}$. The eigenvalues are real, and the method given in this section applies if there is one eigenvalue of maximum modulus.

(c) For the general complex matrix the method, given in this section applies, provided there is one eigenvalue of maximum modulus, though, as in (a), it is necessary to introduce biorthogonal functions in the theory.

Suppose that u_0 is an arbitrary $n \times 1$ column matrix. By successive premultiplication by A form the sequence

$$u_1 = Au_0, \quad u_2 = Au_1 = A^2 u_0,$$

$$u_p = Au_{p-1} = A^p u_0. \tag{6.11}$$

(The suffix p in u_p is used in a different sense from the suffix i in x_i. This distinction should be borne in mind throughout this section.)   On assuming a representation of the form (6.9) for u_0 and using (6.5) we see that

$$u_1 = Au_0 = a_1 \lambda_1 x_1 + a_2 \lambda_2 x_2 + \ldots + a_n \lambda_n x_n,$$

$$u_p = A^p u_0 = a_1 \lambda_1^p x_1 + a_2 \lambda_2^p x_2 + \ldots + a_n \lambda_n^p x_n \tag{6.12}$$

$$= \lambda_1^p \left\{ a_1 x_1 + \sum_{i=2}^{n} a_i \left(\frac{\lambda_i}{\lambda_1} \right)^p x_i \right\}. \tag{6.13}$$

Suppose next that $|\lambda_1| > |\lambda_2| \geqq |\lambda_3| \geqq ... \geqq |\lambda_n|$. Then $(\lambda_i/\lambda_1)^p$ tends to zero as p tends to infinity $(i>1)$. If u_p, x_i are the sth elements of u_p, x_i for some specific s, and we define

$$l_p = u_p/u_{p-1}, \qquad (6.14)$$

we find

$$l_p = \lambda_1 \left\{ \frac{1 + \sum_{i=2}^{n} B_i \left(\frac{\lambda_i}{\lambda_1}\right)^p}{1 + \sum_{i=2}^{n} B_i \left(\frac{\lambda_i}{\lambda_1}\right)^{p-1}} \right\} \to \lambda_1 \text{ as } p \to \infty, \quad (6.15)$$

where $B_i = a_i x_i / a_1 x_1$. In deriving this result we have made two important assumptions:

  (i) There is only one eigenvalue with largest modulus. The general case is outside the scope of this book (cf. Exs. 6.7, 6.8).
  (ii) The trial vector u_0 is such that $a_1 \neq 0$. For rapid convergence we should try to choose u_0 so that a_1 is as large as possible relative to the other a_i. The approximate form of u_0 is often known on physical grounds.

In numerical work, instead of working with the sequence u_p it is convenient to form the sequences z_p, w_p, starting from an arbitrary vector $z_0 = l_0 w_0$, by means of the equations

$$A w_{p-1} = z_p = l_p w_p, \quad (p = 1, 2, 3, ...), \qquad (6.16)$$

where l_p is now defined as the largest element of z_p, so that the largest element of w_p is unity. Suppose that the largest element of x_1 is the sth element and that x_1 is normalised so that this element is unity. A minor difficulty arises in the theoretical analysis because for small p the largest element of z_p (and hence the unit element of w_p) may not be the sth element due to the preponderance of components other than x_1 in the initial trial vector. But we know, from assumption (ii) above, that eventually the effect of x_1 will predominate. Hence without loss of generality we can assume that the sth element of z_p is always the largest element. We write

$$w_0 = \left\{ x_1 + \sum_{i=2}^{n} \alpha_i x_i \right\} \Big/ \left\{ 1 + \sum_{i=2}^{n} \alpha_i x_i \right\},$$

where we denote the sth element of $x_i (i > 1)$ by x_i, and the α_i are constants whose precise values are not important. From (6.16) we find

$$w_p = \left\{ x_1 + \sum_{=2}^{n} \alpha_i \left(\frac{\lambda_i}{\lambda_1} \right)^p x_i \right\} \Big/ \left\{ 1 + \sum_{i=2}^{n} \alpha_i \left(\frac{\lambda_i}{\lambda_1} \right)^p x_i \right\}, \quad (6.17)$$

$$l_p = \lambda_1 \left\{ 1 + \sum_{i=2}^{n} \alpha_i \left(\frac{\lambda_i}{\lambda_1} \right)^p x_i \right\} \Big/ \left\{ 1 + \sum_{i=2}^{n} \alpha_i \left(\frac{\lambda_i}{\lambda_1} \right)^{p-1} x_i \right\}.$$

As before l_p tends to λ_1 as p tends to infinity. Also w_p tends to x_1.

If convergence is slow it will be desirable to use extrapolation. In order to simplify the analysis we make a third assumption:

(iii) $\lambda_2 \neq -\lambda_3.$ (6.18)

(We have already assumed $|\lambda_2| \geqq |\lambda_3|$. This new assumption imposes an additional restriction.) On using this assumption we have, for sufficiently large p,

$$l_p \approx \lambda_1 \left\{ \frac{1 + \alpha_2 x_2 (\lambda_2/\lambda_1)^p}{1 + \alpha_2 x_2 (\lambda_2/\lambda_1)^{p-1}} \right\} \approx \lambda_1 \{ 1 + k(\lambda_2/\lambda_1)^p \},$$

where $k = \alpha_2 x_2 (\lambda_2 - \lambda_1)/\lambda_2$. An improved approximation L_1 for λ_1 can be obtained by setting

$$l_p = L_1 \{ 1 + k(\lambda_2/\lambda_1)^p \}.$$ (6.19)

On replacing p by $p-1$ and eliminating k we find

$$L_1 - l_p = (\lambda_2/\lambda_1)(L_1 - l_{p-1}).$$ (6.20)

Hence in the terminology of § 2.4 we are dealing with a first-order iterative procedure. Convergence can be accelerated by using Aitken's δ^2-process (2.15). (Compare (6.20) and (2.13).) An improved estimate of λ_1 is therefore given by

$$L_1 = l_p - \frac{(l_p - l_{p-1})^2}{l_p - 2l_{p-1} + l_{p-2}}. \qquad (6.21)$$

In exactly the same way (6.17) gives

$$w_p \approx x_1 + k(\lambda_2/\lambda_1)^p, \quad \text{where } k = \alpha_2\{x_2 - (\lambda_1/\lambda_2)x_2x_1\}.$$

Hence convergence of the successive approximate eigenvectors can also be accelerated by using Aitken's δ^2-process. But it must be remembered that the above analysis is not valid if $\lambda_2 = -\lambda_3$, and the extrapolation will not be very accurate if λ_2 is approximately equal to $-\lambda_3$.

In applying Aitken's formula it is essential that no numerical mistakes be made in computing the iterates used. For the special case when A is symmetrical a numerical check on successive iterates is given by the following formula derived from (6.16):

$$l_{p+1}w'_{p-1}w_{p+1} = l_p w'_p w_p. \qquad (6.22)$$

From (6.20) it is clear that the rate of convergence of the original first-order iterative procedure depends on λ_1/λ_2. The larger this ratio the faster the convergence. From (6.19) it is seen that

$$\frac{\lambda_1}{\lambda_2} \approx \frac{l_{p-1} - l_{p-2}}{l_p - l_{p-1}} = t_p, \text{ say}. \qquad (6.23)$$

The value of t_p can similarly be estimated from the components of w_{p-2}, w_{p-1}, w_p. In terms of t_p Aitken's formula (6.21) is (cf. (2.18b)):

$$L_1 = l_p + \frac{1}{t_p - 1}(l_p - l_{p-1}).$$

K

In hand computation it is often convenient to compute t_p mentally after each iteration and extrapolate using Aitken's formula as soon as successive iterates begin to vary regularly, as indicated by agreement between successive values of t_p. If successive values of t_p show no signs of behaving regularly as p increases this indicates that some of the basic assumptions (i)-(iii) in the above analysis are wrong (cf. Exs. 6.7, 6.8).

Ex. 6.2. *Obtain the largest eigenvalue and the corresponding eigenvector of the following matrix, working to four decimal places*:

$$A = \begin{bmatrix} -0\cdot030 & -0\cdot242 & -0\cdot603 & 0\cdot178 \\ -0\cdot242 & 0\cdot860 & -0\cdot343 & 0\cdot393 \\ -0\cdot603 & -0\cdot343 & 1\cdot350 & 0\cdot251 \\ 0\cdot178 & 0\cdot393 & 0\cdot251 & 2\cdot630 \end{bmatrix} \quad (6.24)$$

Iteration with $w'_0 = [1, 1, 1, 1]$ gives

$$z_6 = 2\cdot7386 \begin{bmatrix} 0\cdot0180 \\ 0\cdot1808 \\ 0\cdot1349 \\ 1\cdot0000 \end{bmatrix}, \quad z_7 = 2\cdot7381 \begin{bmatrix} 0\cdot0191 \\ 0\cdot1818 \\ 0\cdot1316 \\ 1\cdot0000 \end{bmatrix}, \quad z_8 = 2\cdot7379 \begin{bmatrix} 0\cdot0198 \\ 0\cdot1825 \\ 0\cdot1296 \\ 1\cdot0000 \end{bmatrix}.$$

The numerical check (6.22) gives $l_8 w'_6 w_8 = 2\cdot8770_8$ and $l_7 w'_7 w_7 = 2\cdot8770_2$. The following values of $t_3 \ldots t_8$ are found: -17, $-2\cdot2$, 12, $1\cdot1$, $3\cdot0$, $2\cdot5$. The last two values are not very accurate due to round-off error. However, the values of t_p indicate that successive iterates are beginning to behave regularly when $p = 8$ and this can be confirmed by estimating t_p from the components of the eigenvectors. Since the round-off error is starting to become appreciable compared with the differences between successive iterates z_6, z_7, z_8 it is advisable to apply Aitken's δ^2-process at this

point. (If we were working to five or more decimal places
we might iterate again to confirm the regular behaviour.)
We obtain

$$x_1 = \begin{bmatrix} 0\cdot0198+0\cdot0012 \\ 0\cdot1825+0\cdot0016 \\ 0\cdot1296-0\cdot0031 \\ 1\cdot0000 \end{bmatrix} = \begin{bmatrix} 0\cdot0210 \\ 0\cdot1841 \\ 0\cdot1265 \\ 1\cdot0000 \end{bmatrix}.$$

A further two iterations give

$$\lambda_1 = 2\cdot7376, \quad x_1 = \begin{bmatrix} 0\cdot0207 \\ 0\cdot1836 \\ 0\cdot1265 \\ 1\cdot0000 \end{bmatrix}.$$

Further iteration merely repeats these values which therefore
represent the final estimate of the solution.

§ 6.3. **The determination of subdominant eigenvalues and
eigenvectors.** When the largest or dominant eigenvalue
and the corresponding eigenvector of an $n \times n$ matrix has
been obtained various methods are available for replacing
the matrix by an $(n-1) \times (n-1)$ matrix with eigenvalues
$\lambda_2 \ldots \lambda_n$. The largest eigenvalue and corresponding eigenvector of this new matrix can then be determined. The
procedure can be repeated until all the eigenvalues and
eigenvectors of the original matrix have been determined.
We confine our attention to the case of a real symmetric
matrix with real, distinct, eigenvalues.

The method described below applies only to symmetric
matrices. It depends essentially on the orthogonality
property of eigenvectors given by equation (6.7). The
method is described sufficiently clearly by an example, and
we give no general discussion. Other methods for removing
known eigenvalues and eigenvectors from a matrix are

described in *Modern Computing Methods*, H.M. Stationery
Office, 2nd Edn. (1961), Chapter III.

Ex. 6.3. Suppose that the second largest eigenvector of the
matrix used in Ex. 6.2 is given by $x'_2 = [x_1, x_2, x_3, x_4]$.
From the equation $x'_2 x_1 = 0$ using the value found in
Ex. 6.2 for x_1 we find

$$x_4 = -0{\cdot}0207x_1 - 0{\cdot}1836x_2 - 0{\cdot}1265x_3. \quad (6.25)$$

If we write out in full the first linear equation of the matrix
system $Ax = \lambda x$ where A is the matrix of Ex. 6.2, we have

$$-0{\cdot}030x_1 - 0{\cdot}242x_2 - 0{\cdot}603x_3 + 0{\cdot}178x_4 = \lambda x_1.$$

The unknown x_4 can be eliminated from this equation by
means of (6.25). In the same way x_4 can be eliminated
from the left-hand sides of the other three equations in
$Ax = \lambda x$, and finally we obtain

$$-0{\cdot}0337x_1 - 0{\cdot}2747x_2 - 0{\cdot}6255x_3 = \lambda x_1, \quad (6.26a)$$

$$-0{\cdot}2501x_1 + 0{\cdot}7878x_2 - 0{\cdot}3927x_3 = \lambda x_2, \quad (6.26b)$$

$$-0{\cdot}6082x_1 - 0{\cdot}3891x_2 + 1{\cdot}3182x_3 = \lambda x_3, \quad (6.26c)$$

$$0{\cdot}1236x_1 - 0{\cdot}0899x_2 - 0{\cdot}0817x_3 = \lambda x_4. \quad (6.26d)$$

The first three equations represent an eigenvalue problem
for the 3×3 matrix

$$B = \begin{bmatrix} -0{\cdot}0337 & -0{\cdot}2747 & -0{\cdot}6255 \\ -0{\cdot}2501 & +0{\cdot}7878 & -0{\cdot}3927 \\ -0{\cdot}6082 & -0{\cdot}3891 & +1{\cdot}3182 \end{bmatrix}. \quad (6.27)$$

Suppose that the largest eigenvalue and the corresponding
eigenvector of the matrix (6.27) has been found by the
method of § 6.2 or otherwise. From the values of x_1, x_2, x_3
the value of x_4 can be found from (6.25) and the final values
of the x_i can be checked from (6.26d) or vice-versa. In this

way we obtain

$$\lambda_2 = 1 \cdot 6500, \quad x_2 = \begin{bmatrix} -0 \cdot 3119 \\ -0 \cdot 3650 \\ 1 \cdot 0000 \\ -0 \cdot 0530 \end{bmatrix}.$$

Suppose next that $[y_1, y_2, y_3, y_4]$ denotes the transpose of one of the two remaining eigenvectors x_3 or x_4. This vector is orthogonal to x_1 and x_2 which are now known, so that

$$-0 \cdot 3119 y_1 - 0 \cdot 3650 y_2 + 1 \cdot 0000 y_3 - 0 \cdot 0530 y_4 = 0,$$

$$0 \cdot 0207 y_1 + 0 \cdot 1836 y_2 + 0 \cdot 1265 y_3 + 1 \cdot 0000 y_4 = 0. \quad (6.28)$$

Elimination of y_4 between these two equations gives

$$y_3 = 0 \cdot 3087 y_1 + 0 \cdot 3529 y_2. \quad (6.29)$$

On recalling the method of derivation of (6.26) we see that (6.26) still hold if the x_i are replaced by y_i. If in (6.26a-c) we eliminate y_3 by means of (6.29) we obtain

$$-0 \cdot 2268 y_1 - 0 \cdot 4954 y_2 = \lambda y_1,$$

$$-0 \cdot 3713 y_1 + 0 \cdot 6492 y_2 = \lambda y_2,$$

$$-0 \cdot 2013 y_1 + 0 \cdot 0761 y_2 = \lambda y_3. \quad (6.30)$$

The first two equations represent an eigenvalue problem for the 2×2 matrix

$$C = \begin{bmatrix} -0 \cdot 2268 & -0 \cdot 4954 \\ -0 \cdot 3713 & 0 \cdot 6492 \end{bmatrix}.$$

The easiest method of procedure is now to solve the eigenvalue problem det $[C - \lambda I] = 0$ by expansion of the determinant and direct solution of the resulting quadratic. Back-substitution in (6.29) and (6.28) give the remaining components of the eigenvectors of the original matrix A

and (6.30) is a check. This gives, on normalising so that
the largest elements are unity,

$$\lambda_3 = 0\cdot8241, \quad x_3 = \begin{bmatrix} -0\cdot4714 \\ 1\cdot0000 \\ 0\cdot2074 \\ -0\cdot2001 \end{bmatrix} : \quad \lambda_4 = -0\cdot4017, \quad x_4 = \begin{bmatrix} 1\cdot0000 \\ 0\cdot3533 \\ 0\cdot4334 \\ -0\cdot1741 \end{bmatrix}.$$

§ 6.4. **The iterative solution of linear simultaneous
algebraic equations.** It is convenient to consider certain
iterative methods for the solution of linear equations at this
point, since the convergence of these procedures can be
discussed by means of the theory of eigenvalues and eigenvectors. We start by stating two classical iterative procedures, considering for simplicity the case of three equations
in three unknowns. It is assumed that the elements in the
principal diagonal of the coefficient matrix are non-zero.
Without loss of generality these can be taken to be unity.

(a) The equations for the **method of simultaneous
corrections** are

$$\begin{aligned}
x_1^{(r+1)} &= \phantom{-a_{21}x_1^{(r)}} -a_{12}x_2^{(r)} \phantom{-a_{13}x_3^{(r)}} -a_{13}x_3^{(r)}+b_1, \\
x_2^{(r+1)} &= -a_{21}x_1^{(r)} \phantom{-a_{12}x_2^{(r)}} -a_{23}x_3^{(r)}+b_2, \quad (6.31) \\
x_3^{(r+1)} &= -a_{31}x_1^{(r)} \quad -a_{32}x_2^{(r)} \phantom{-a_{23}x_3^{(r)}} +b_3.
\end{aligned}$$

(b) The equations for the **method of successive corrections** are

$$\begin{aligned}
x_1^{(r+1)} &= \phantom{-a_{21}x_1^{(r+1)}} -a_{12}x_2^{(r)} \phantom{-a_{13}x_3^{(r)}} -a_{13}x_3^{(r)}+b_1, \\
x_2^{(r+1)} &= -a_{21}x_1^{(r+1)} \phantom{-a_{12}x_2^{(r)}} -a_{23}x_3^{(r)}+b_2, \quad (6.32) \\
x_3^{(r+1)} &= -a_{31}x_1^{(r+1)}-a_{32}x_2^{(r+1)} \phantom{-a_{23}x_3^{(r)}} +b_3.
\end{aligned}$$

The new estimates of the x_i are used on the right
as soon as they are obtained.

A general class of iterative procedures, which includes these methods as special cases, can be discussed in the following way. We solve the equations

$$Ax = b, \qquad (6.33)$$

where A is an $n \times n$ matrix, by splitting the matrix A in the form $A = E - F$. Then

$$Ex = Fx + b, \qquad (6.34)$$

and an iterative procedure is derived by writing

$$Ex^{(r+1)} = Fx^{(r)} + b, \qquad (6.35)$$

where $x^{(r)}$ is the rth approximation to the exact value x. The iteration is started by setting $x^{(0)}$ equal to an arbitrary column matrix. If it is possible to obtain an approximation to the exact solution x it may be convenient to take $x^{(0)}$ equal to this estimate of x but often it is sufficient to choose $x^{(0)} = 0$. The matrix E should be chosen so that it is easy to solve the set of equations (6.35) for $x^{(r+1)}$, assuming that $x^{(r)}$ is known. This implies that det E is non-zero, and E^{-1} exists. We have seen in Chapter V that it is easy to solve sets of equations if the matrix of coefficients is of lower triangular form, and E is often chosen to be of this type. An example is the method of successive corrections quoted above.

Instead of working in terms of the estimated values of the unknowns it is useful to introduce the corrections

$$c^{(r+1)} = x^{(r+1)} - x^{(r)}. \qquad (6.36)$$

As in the discussion of other types of iterative procedure in Chapter II, if $x^{(r)}$ tends to the required value x as r tends to infinity we say that the procedure is convergent. If the procedure is convergent

$$x = x^{(0)} + \sum_{r=1}^{\infty} c^{(r)}. \qquad (6.37)$$

A necessary condition for convergence of the infinite series in this equation is that $c^{(r)}$ should tend to zero as r tends to infinity. On writing $r-1$ in place of r in (6.35) and subtracting the result from (6.35) we see that

$$c^{(r+1)} = Kc^{(r)}, \quad \text{where } K = E^{-1}F. \tag{6.38}$$

Hence

$$c^{(r+1)} = K^{r+1}c^{(0)}. \tag{6.39}$$

The convergence of the procedure therefore depends on the behaviour of K^r as r tends to infinity. This can be expressed in terms of the size of the eigenvalues of K by the following argument which should be compared with the analysis at the beginning of § 6.2. We consider only the case where the matrix K possesses n linearly independent eigenfunctions z_i with corresponding eigenvalues λ_i, so that

$$Kz_i = \lambda_i z_i, \quad \text{or} \quad (F-\lambda_i E)z_i = 0. \tag{6.40}$$

It is assumed that there is one eigenvalue of maximum modulus, say λ_1, where λ_1 is real. The other eigenvalues can be complex. From (6.9) the vector $c^{(0)}$ can be written in the form

$$c^{(0)} = a_1 z_1 + a_2 z_2 + \ldots + a_n z_n. \tag{6.41}$$

From (6.39), (6.40), (6.41),

$$c^{(r+1)} = a_1 \lambda_1^{r+1} z_1 + a_2 \lambda_2^{r+1} z_2 + \ldots + a_n \lambda_n^{r+1} z_n. \tag{6.42}$$

For large r, R, since λ_1 is the eigenvalue of largest modulus,

$$c^{(r+1)} \approx a_1 \lambda_1^{r+1} z_1, \quad c^{(R+s)} \approx \lambda_1^s c^{(R)}. \tag{6.43}$$

If we perform R iterations and then estimate $c^{(R+s)}$ for $s>0$ by means of this result, equation (6.37) gives

$$x = x^{(0)} + \sum_{r=1}^{R} c^{(r)} + c^*, \tag{6.44a}$$

where

$$c^* = \sum_{r=R+1}^{\infty} c^{(r)} \approx c^{(R)} \sum_{S=1}^{\infty} \lambda_1^s = \frac{\lambda_1}{1-\lambda_1} c^{(R)}. \tag{6.44b}$$

We have assumed that $|\lambda_1| < 1$, and this is obviously a necessary condition for convergence of the procedure. This formula provides an estimate of the error at any stage of the iterative procedure provided that there is one real eigenvalue λ_1 which is larger in modulus than the others, and the approximate value of λ_1 is known. From (6.43) the value of λ_1 can be estimated from the ratio of corresponding elements of successive $c^{(r)}$. The consistency of the values of λ_1 obtained at various stages of the iteration is an essential check on the validity of the basic assumption that there is one eigenvalue which is larger in modulus than the others.

We define the **rate of convergence** ρ by the formula

$$\rho = -\ln|\lambda_1|, \qquad (6.45)$$

where λ_1 is the eigenvalue of K with the largest modulus, as defined in the last paragraph. To illustrate the significance of ρ we introduce the error vector

$$e^{(r)} = x^{(r)} - x.$$

Subtraction of (6.33) from (6.35) gives

$$e^{(r+1)} = Ke^{(r)} = K^{r+1}e^{(0)}.$$

As in the analysis leading to (6.43) we can show that for large r the error in any component of the rth iterate will be nearly equal to $\lambda_1^r p$, where p is some constant. The number of iterations required to reduce the error in this component to, say, ε is given by

$$|\lambda_1^r p| \approx \varepsilon.$$

Taking logarithms

$$r \approx \frac{\ln(|p|/\varepsilon)}{-\ln|\lambda_1|} = \frac{\ln(|p|/\varepsilon)}{\rho}.$$

Hence the number of iterations required is inversely proportional to the rate of convergence. The smaller the value of $|\lambda_1|$ the greater the rate of convergence.

We can compare the rates of convergence of different iterative procedures for solving the same set of equations if we can compare the magnitudes of the eigenvalues of maximum modulus of the corresponding matrices. An instructive elementary discussion of rates of convergence can be given for the special case of a **band** or **tridiagonal** matrix, the elements of which are zero except on the principal and immediately adjacent diagonals. Without loss of generality we can assume that the principal diagonal elements are unity so that we can set

$$A = L + I + U$$

where I is the unit matrix and in the 3×3 case we can set

$$A = \begin{bmatrix} 1 & u_1 & 0 \\ l_1 & 1 & u_2 \\ 0 & l_2 & 1 \end{bmatrix}, \quad L = \begin{bmatrix} 0 & 0 & 0 \\ l_1 & 0 & 0 \\ 0 & l_2 & 0 \end{bmatrix}, \quad U = \begin{bmatrix} 0 & u_1 & 0 \\ 0 & 0 & u_2 \\ 0 & 0 & 0 \end{bmatrix}.$$

The methods of simultaneous and successive corrections, equations (6.31), (6.32), can be written, respectively,

$$x^{(r+1)} = -(L+U)x^{(r)} + b, \qquad (6.46)$$

$$(L+I)x^{(r+1)} = -Ux^{(r)} + b. \qquad (6.47)$$

We examine a generalisation of (6.47) which, as explained later, is known as the **method of successive over-corrections**:

$$(L + pI)x^{(r+1)} = -\{(1-p)I + U\}x^{(r)} + b, \qquad (6.48)$$

where p is a constant which will be determined so as to yield the fastest rate of convergence. The method of successive corrections is the special case $p = 1$. We shall compare the rates of convergence of (6.46) and (6.48). From (6.34), (6.40), (6.45) this means that we need to compare the eigenvalues λ, μ defined by the equations

$$(6.46): \qquad [(L+U) + \lambda I]u = 0, \qquad (6.49)$$

$$(6.48): \qquad [\{(1-p)I + U\} + \mu(L+pI)]v = 0. \qquad (6.50)$$

By means of the following procedure we can show that λ and μ are directly related. Write (6.50) out in detail. Multiply the ith equation by $\alpha_i (i = 1, 2, 3)$ and set

$$P = (1-p)+p\mu,$$
$$v_j = \beta_j V_j, \quad (j = 1, 2, 3),$$

where the V_j are new unknowns. The α_i, β_j are constants which are at our disposal. The equations (6.50) become

$$P\alpha_1\beta_1 V_1 + u_1\alpha_1\beta_2 V_2 \qquad\qquad = 0,$$
$$\mu l_1\alpha_2\beta_1 V_1 + P\alpha_2\beta_2 V_2 + u_2\alpha_2\beta_3 V_3 = 0, \qquad (6.51)$$
$$\mu l_2\alpha_3\beta_2 V_2 + \; P\alpha_3\beta_3 V_3 = 0.$$

We next identify these equations with (6.49). To make the terms off the principal diagonal agree, we require

$$\alpha_1\beta_2 \; = \alpha_2\beta_3 \; = 1,$$
$$\alpha_2\beta_1\mu = \alpha_3\beta_2\mu = 1.$$

By means of these equations, four of the six α_i, β_j can be expressed in terms of the remaining two. The way in which this is done is immaterial. Suppose that we set

$$\beta_2 = \alpha_1^{-1}, \quad \beta_3 = \alpha_2^{-1}, \quad \beta_1 = (\alpha_2\mu)^{-1}, \quad \alpha_3 = \alpha_1\mu^{-1}.$$

Then (6.51) become

$$(\alpha_1/\alpha_2)P\mu^{-1}V_1 + \qquad u_1 V_2 \qquad\qquad = 0,$$
$$l_1 V_1 + (\alpha_2/\alpha_1)PV_2 + \qquad u_2 V_3 = 0,$$
$$l_2 V_2 + (\alpha_1/\alpha_2)P\mu^{-1}V_3 = 0.$$

These are identical with (6.49) if

$$\alpha_1/\alpha_2 = \mu^{\frac{1}{2}}, \quad V = u$$
$$P = (1-p)+p\mu = \mu^{\frac{1}{2}}\lambda. \qquad (6.52)$$

First of all we consider the method of successive corrections, $p = 1$. Then (6.52) gives $\mu = \lambda^2$. This result shows that in the case of a band matrix the eigenvalues for the method of successive corrections are the squares of those for simultaneous corrections. Hence for a given problem involving a band matrix the two methods both converge or they both diverge. If they converge, the rate of convergence is doubled if we use successive instead of simultaneous corrections.

To determine the value of p which gives the fastest rate of convergence for any given λ we discuss the dependence of the roots of the quadratic (6.52) for $\mu^{\frac{1}{2}}$ on p. When the roots are real we need to consider the root of larger modulus, namely

$$|\mu^{\frac{1}{2}}| = (2p)^{-1}\{|\lambda| + \sqrt{(\lambda^2 - 4p + 4p^2)}\}, \quad p_1 < p < p_2, \quad (6.53)$$

where p_1, p_2 are the roots of the quadratic $4p^2 - 4p + \lambda^2 = 0$. For $0 < |\lambda| < 1$ we have $0 < p_1 < \frac{1}{2} < p_2 < 1$. When the roots are complex

$$|\mu| = (p^{-1} - 1), \quad p_1 < p < p_2. \quad (6.54)$$

By drawing graphs of $|\mu|$ against p for various λ it is easy to see that for convergence we need consider only $p > \frac{1}{2}$, and then $|\mu|$ decreases for $\frac{1}{2} < p < p_2$, and increases for $p > p_2$. Also the largest $|\mu|$ corresponds to the largest $|\lambda|$. Hence the rate of convergence is greatest when

$$p = p_2 = \frac{1}{2}\{1 + \sqrt{(1 - \lambda_1^2)}\}, \quad (6.55)$$

where λ_1 is the root of maximum modulus for the method of simultaneous corrections. From (6.53), (6.54) the eigenvalue of maximum modulus corresponding to the optimum p is given by

$$\mu_1 = (2p)^{-2}\lambda_1^2 = p^{-1} - 1$$

$$= \{1 - \sqrt{(1 - \lambda_1^2)}\}\{1 + \sqrt{(1 - \lambda_1^2)}\}^{-1}. \quad (6.56)$$

The value of the method can be illustrated by supposing that $\lambda_1 = 1 - \varepsilon$ where ε is small so that the methods of successive and simultaneous corrections converge slowly. Then

$$\mu_1 \approx \{1 - \sqrt{(2\varepsilon)}\}\{1 + \sqrt{(2\varepsilon)}\}^{-1} \approx 1 - 2\sqrt{(2\varepsilon)}.$$

If $\lambda_1 = 0 \cdot 995$, $\varepsilon = 0 \cdot 005$, then $\mu_1 \approx 0 \cdot 8$ and a remarkable increase in the rate of convergence is obtained.

We can rearrange (6.48) in the form

$$x^{(r+1)} = x^{(r)} + \omega\{-Lx^{(r+1)} - (I+U)x^{(r)} - b\}, \quad (6.57)$$

where $\omega = 1/p$. If $p = \omega = 1$ we have the method of successive corrections and the bracketed term on the right is the correction added to $x^{(r)}$ to give $x^{(r+1)}$. From (6.55) since $|\lambda_1| < |$ we have $\tfrac{1}{2} < p < 1$, or $\omega > 1$, so that in the general method the bracketed term is multiplied by a factor greater than unity. This is the reason for naming the procedure the method of successive over-corrections.

The following example illustrates numerically some aspects of the iterative procedures described in this section. An application of these methods is given in Ex. 11.9.

Ex. 6.4. *Obtain the results given in Table* 6.1. *for iterative solution of the following equations, working to five decimal places.*

$$
\begin{aligned}
20x_1 - 8x_2 \quad\quad\quad\quad &= 6, \\
-4x_1 + 20x_2 - 4x_3 \quad\quad &= 6, \quad\quad (6.58) \\
-4x_2 + 19x_3 - 4x_4 &= 5, \\
-8x_3 + 20x_4 &= 1.
\end{aligned}
$$

In all cases the iteration was started with the estimates

$$20x_1^{(0)} = 6, \quad 20x_2^{(0)} = 6, \quad 19x_3^{(0)} = 5, \quad 20x_4^{(0)} = 1.$$

The eigenvalue of maximum modulus was estimated from

$$\lambda_1 \approx \left\{ \sum_{i=1}^{4} c_i^{(r+1)} \right\} \bigg/ \left\{ \sum_{i=1}^{4} c_i^{(r)} \right\}, \quad r = 3, 4.$$

For the methods of simultaneous and successive corrections the results in Table 6.1 give $\lambda_1 \approx 0.4$ and $\lambda_1 \approx 0.2$ respectively, though the iteration in the latter case has not proceeded far enough to give an accurate estimate. The c_i^* in Table 6.1

TABLE 6.1

Results for the iterative solution of (6.58).
All figures have been multiplied by 10^5.

Method	i	$c_i^{(3)}$	$c_i^{(4)}$	$c_i^{(5)}$	c_i^*	Estimated x_i	Error
Simult. correct. (6.31)	1	1550	727	239	160	491 81	−30
	2	1818	597	299	200	480 51	+24
	3	1436	769	247	165	408 89	−37
	4	1835	574	308	206	213 97	+27
Success. correct. (6.32)	1	1257	400	74	18	492 14	+3
	2	999	185	31	8	480 28	+1
	3	525	83	13	3	409 25	−1
	4	210	33	5	1	213 69	−1
Success. over-correct. (6.57) $\omega = 1.044$.	1	918	297	15	1	492 11	0
	2	809	68	4	0	480 28	+1
	3	197	17	1	0	409 26	0
	4	47	5	0	0	213 70	0

are then obtained from (6.44b). For the method of successive over-corrections we use, from (6.55) with $\lambda_1 = 0.4$,

$$\omega = 1/p = 2\{1 + \sqrt{0.84}\}^{-1} \approx 1.044.$$

In practice, of course, when ω is estimated, we should not start from the beginning again with the original $x_i^{(0)}$ as we have done in Table 6.1, but we should start from the currently available estimates of the x_i.

In computing by hand, since the result is obtained by

adding corrections and the accuracy of the extrapolation also depends on the accuracy of the corrections, it is essential to apply checks. Consider the method of successive corrections applied to a 3×3 set of equations in (6.32). On adding the equations and subtracting from the result the corresponding equations with $r - 1$ in place of r we have

$$(1 + a_{21} + a_{31})c_1^{(r+1)} + (1 + a_{32})c_2^{(r+1)} + c_3^{(r+1)}$$
$$= -a_{12}c_2^{(r)} - (a_{13} + a_{23})c_3^{(r)},$$

where $c_i^{(r)}$ is the ith component of $c^{(r)}$. A final check should also be applied by carrying out one iteration with the final estimates of the x_i.

Examples VI

Ex. 6.5. Show that the sum of the eigenvalues of A equals the sum of the diagonal elements of A and the product of the eigenvalues is equal to det A. If the matrix A has distinct non-zero eigenvalues λ_i show that A^{-1}, A^2 have eigenvalues λ_i^{-1}, λ_i^2 respectively, and that A, A^{-1}, A^2 have the same eigenvectors.

Ex. 6.6. Prove the following statements. The matrices $A - \mu I$ and A have the same eigenvectors. If η is an eigenvalue of $A - \mu I$ then $\mu + \eta$ is an eigenvalue of A. To find the largest eigenvalue of A by the first-order iterative procedure of § 6.2 it is in general quicker to iterate with $A - \mu I$ rather than A, for some suitable choice of μ. Suppose that λ_1 is positive and that the eigenvalues are arranged in the order $\lambda_1 > \lambda_2 \geqq \ldots \geqq \lambda_n$ with $|\lambda_1| > |\lambda_2|$ and $|\lambda_1| > |\lambda_n|$. The fastest rate of convergence is obtained when μ is chosen equal to $\frac{1}{2}(\lambda_2 + \lambda_n)$. For this choice of μ assumption (iii) of § 6.2 is no longer valid and if it is desired to use Aitken's δ^2-process it may be better to choose $\mu = \frac{1}{2}(\lambda_3 + \lambda_n)$. The difficulty in applying these results is of course that λ_2, λ_3, λ_n are usually not known.

When using an automatic computer it may be worthwhile
to find a suitable value of μ empirically. If it is known that
all the roots are positive then a simple choice for μ is
$\frac{1}{3}\lambda_1^*$ where λ_1^* is an approximate value for λ_1 found by
iteration, using A. The above device can be used to find
the smallest eigenvalue λ_n of A by choosing $\mu = \frac{1}{2}(\lambda_1 + \lambda_{n-1})$
or $\frac{1}{2}(\lambda_1 + \lambda_{n-2})$. This procedure may not be very satisfactory if the lowest roots are close together, which is often
the case.

Illustrate these remarks by discussing the case of a fourth-
order matrix with eigenvalues 4, 3, 2, 1.

Ex. 6.7. Show that if $\lambda_1 = -\lambda_2$ then, using the same
notation as in § 6.2,

$$u_{2s} \approx \lambda_1^{2s}(a_1 x_1 + a_2 x_2),$$

$$u_{2s+1} \approx \lambda_1^{2s}(a_1 x_1 - a_2 x_2).$$

Deduce that if u_p is any element of $\mathbf{u}_p$ then u_p/u_{p-2} tends to
λ_1^2 as p tends to infinity and show how x_1 and x_2 can be
found.

Show that if $|\lambda_1| > |\lambda_2|$ and $\lambda_2 = -\lambda_3$ so that assump-
tion (iii) of § 6.2 is not true, Aitken's δ^2-process can be
applied to even or odd order iterates, but not to any three
successive iterates.

Ex. 6.8. If the dominant eigenvalues of A are complex
conjugate, suppose that they are the roots of $\lambda^2 + \alpha\lambda + \beta = 0$.
Show that for sufficiently large p

$$u_p + \alpha u_{p-1} + \beta u_{p-2} = 0.$$

Deduce a method for finding α, β, and hence the dominant
eigenvalues of A.

Ex. 6.9. In order to understand the emphasis on
symmetrical matrices in this chapter we indicate how the

theory of orthogonality of eigenvectors must be modified when A is unsymmetrical. Proofs of the following statements are left to the reader. A and its transpose A' have the same eigenvalues λ_i and we assume that these are distinct. Corresponding to each λ_i there are eigenvectors x_i of A and y_i of A', and in general these are different:

$$Ax_i = \lambda_i x_i, \quad A'y_i = \lambda_i y_i.$$

In general the x_i are not orthogonal to each other, nor are the y_i, but

$$y_i'x_j = 0, \quad (i \neq j).$$

We say that the x_i and y_i are **biorthogonal**. An expansion of the form (6.9) exists for an arbitrary vector. Starting from arbitrary vectors u_0, v_0 we can form two sequences

$$u_p = Au_{p-1}, \quad v_p = A'v_{p-1}.$$

If u_p, v_p are any elements of u_p, v_p then

$$\lim_{p \to \infty} \frac{u_p}{u_{p-1}} = \lambda_1, \quad \lim_{p \to \infty} \frac{v_p}{v_{p-1}} = \lambda_1.$$

Further discussion of the unsymmetrical case lies outside the scope of this book.

Ex. 6.10. Show by doing the necessary numerical work that when finding the dominant eigenvalue of the matrix (6.10) by iterating with $u_0' = [1, 1, 1]$ the rate of convergence is more rapid than would be expected from the ratio λ_2/λ_1. Show that if we use $u_0' = [1, 0, 0]$ the rate of convergence of the eigenvectors is given by λ_2/λ_1 but the rate of convergence of the eigenvalue is again more rapid than might be expected. Explain the reasons for these results.

L

Ex. 6.11. Show that the eigenvalues of the matrix

$$A = \begin{bmatrix} 0 & 1 & 0 & \cdots & 0 & 0 \\ 0 & 0 & 1 & \cdots & 0 & 0 \\ & & \cdot & & \cdot & \\ 0 & 0 & 0 & & 0 & 1 \\ -a_n & -a_{n-1} & -a_{n-2} & \cdots & -a_2 & -a_1 \end{bmatrix}$$

are identical with the roots of the algebraic equation

$$\lambda^n + a_1 \lambda^{n-1} + \ldots + a_n = 0.$$

(Many of the remarks made in previous chapters in connection with finding the roots of algebraic equations apply to the determination of eigenvalues.)

Ex. 6.12. Show that if x is a first-order approximation to the eigenvector x_1 of A, so that $x = x_1 + \varepsilon z$ where ε is small, then

$$L = \frac{x'Ax}{x'x} = \lambda_1 - C\varepsilon^2 + \text{higher-order terms},$$

so that L is a second-order approximation to λ_1. The quantity L is called the **Rayleigh quotient**.

Ex. 6.13. Write computer programs for finding the largest eigenvalue and the corresponding eigenvector of a matrix A using the following methods:

(a) Iterate using (6.16) until successive estimates of λ_1 and the components of x_1 differ by less than a quantity ε specified in a " Read " statement. If the procedure iterates more than 30 times without achieving convergence, print out the last two sets of results and stop the machine.

(b) Instead of the criterion for convergence in (a) use the criterion that the quantity t_p in (6.23) is positive until the "noise-level" of the calculation is reached (cf. Ex. 3.3).

(c) Use the method in (a) with the following addition. Iterate until successive estimates of λ_1 differ by less than $0{\cdot}01\,\lambda_1^*$ where λ_1^* is the current estimate of λ_1. Compute the quantity t_p in (6.23) and continue the iteration with $(A-\tfrac{1}{3}\lambda_1^* I)$, (Ex. 6.6). Check that the new value of t_p is greater than the old value. Otherwise continue iterating with A.

(d) Use the method in (a) with the following addition. Compute the quantity t_p at each stage $(p\geqq 3)$. If t_p and t_{p-1} differ by less than $0{\cdot}1\,t_p$ apply Aitken's δ^2-process and start the iterative procedure again.

Discuss precautions that could be taken to avoid harmful effects due to the noise-level of the calculation in cases (a), (c), (d). (The fact that the noise-level can upset an orthodox iteration is one of the reasons why we may prefer to use the noise-level itself as the criterion for convergence, as in (b).)

Ex. 6.14. Iterative methods for the solution of $Ax = b$ are particularly useful if A is diagonally dominant i.e. if in any row of the matrix the diagonal element is greater than the sum of the absolute values of the non-diagonal elements. Consider the method of simultaneous corrections. Without loss of generality we can take the diagonal elements to be unity. If we define

$$\sigma_i = \sum_j |a_{ij}|, \quad \sigma = \max_i \sigma_i,$$

where the sum is taken over all non-diagonal elements only, then for diagonal dominance $\sigma < 1$. Let $e^{(r)}(i)$ denote the ith element of the error vector $e^{(r)} = x - x^{(r)}$. If we define

E_r to be the maximum value of $e^{(r)}(i)$ for $i = 1, 2, \ldots n$ then

$$\left| e^{(r)}(i) \right| = \left| \sum_j a_{ij} e^{(r-1)}(j) \right| \leqq E_{r-1} \sum_j \left| a_{ij} \right| \leqq \sigma E_{r-1}.$$

Hence

$$E_r \leqq \sigma E_{r-1} \leqq \sigma^r E_0.$$

Hence the method of simultaneous corrections converges for diagonally dominant matrices and for such matrices the modulus of the largest eigenvalue is less than σ.

Ex. 6.15. If X_0 is an approximate inverse of A, show that if we define

$$X_{r+1} = X_r(2I - AX_r), \quad r = 0, 1, 2, \ldots,$$

then as r tends to infinity X_r tends to A^{-1}. The procedure is second-order. This is an analogue, for matrices, of an iterative procedure for finding the inverse of a scalar, $x = 1/a$. (Set $n = -1$ in the first formula in Ex. 2.10.) A necessary condition for convergence of the scalar procedure is that $\left| 1 - ax_0 \right| < 1$. The analogue for the matrix procedure is that the largest eigenvalue of the matrix $I - AX_0$ must be less than unity in modulus.

Ex. 6.16. Write a computer program for the iterative solution of the equations $Ax = b$ using the method of successive corrections. Start with the approximation $x_i^{(0)} = b_i/a_{ii}$. At each stage of the iteration estimate the eigenvalue of maximum modulus by means of the formula

$$\lambda_1 \approx \lambda_1^{(r+1)} = \left\{ \sum_{i=1}^n \left| c_i^{(r+1)} \right| \right\} \bigg/ \left\{ \sum_{i=1}^n \left| c_i^{(r)} \right| \right\}.$$

($c_i^{(r)}$ is the ith component of $c^{(r)}$ defined in (6.36). This formula can be justified by (6.43).) When successive estimates $\lambda_1^{(r)}, \lambda_1^{(r+1)}$ are such that

$$\left| \lambda_1^{(r+1)} - \lambda_1^{(r)} \right| < \delta \left| \lambda_1^{(r+1)} \right|,$$

where δ is a given number, say $0 \cdot 05$, adopt $\lambda_1^{(r+1)}$ as the required estimate of the eigenvalue of maximum modulus λ_1. Correct the estimate of x by means of (6.44). Iterate four times, starting from the corrected estimate of x, and again apply (6.44). (Do not re-estimate λ_1.) Repeat this procedure until the maximum element of the correction vector C defined in (6.44b) is less than a specified number ε. What provision would you make for non-convergence of the procedure and for non-validity of the correction formula (6.44)? What information would you print out if the procedure does not converge, to indicate why the method has failed? (Ex. 11.9 is concerned with a computer program for the method of successive over-corrections.)

INDEX

PRINTED IN GREAT BRITAIN BY OLIVER AND BOYD LTD., EDINBURGH